THE SALMON

THE NEW NATURALIST

THE SALMON

by

J. W. JONES

D.Sc., Ph.D.,

SENIOR LECTURER IN ZOOLOGY
UNIVERSITY OF LIVERPOOL

———◆———

27 Black-and-White Photographs
24 Diagrams

HARPER & BROTHERS
NEW YORK

To My Parents

CONTENTS

LIST OF PLATES

LIST OF DIAGRAMS

EDITORS' PREFACE

SOME years ago, one of the Editors was present at the showing of a film about Salmon taken in a special observation tank by Dr. Jones. The film revealed many facts and incidents which it would have been impossible to discover in any other way, including the extraordinary behaviour of male parr Salmon, scarcely a handsbreadth long, which rush under the imposing bulk of a pair of adult Salmon on their breeding grounds, and are able to fertilize the hen Salmon's eggs as soon as she extrudes them, even before they are reached by the sperm discharged by the big cock Salmon looming above. It was almost as if Gulliver had managed to consummate a union with a Brobdingnagian lady in bed with her giant lord.

It was as a result of seeing this film that Dr. Jones was later invited to write a New Naturalist Monograph on the Salmon, and the present book is the outcome.

We believe that the result is highly satisfactory. For over twenty years, beginning with a Ph.D. thesis on Salmon, then as Superintendent of the Southern Rivers Branch of the Freshwater Biological Association, as Lecturer in the Zoology Department in Liverpool University, when he worked in collaboration with Mr. G. M. King, Superintendent of the Dee Fishery Board, Dr. Jones has been concerned with the problem of Salmon in every aspect, from the abstrusely scientific to the immediate and the practical. These are of intense interest. Is it true that Salmon never eat while in fresh water? The answer is Yes. But then why do Salmon (sometimes!) rise to the angler's fly. Dr. Jones suggests it may occasionally be in a mood of irritation, or in one of playfulness.

The Salmon divides its existence between river and sea. Was its ancestor a freshwater creature or a marine one? To this Dr. Jones can only give a non-committal answer, but the reader will find the arguments on either side of great interest.

We learn that not so long ago, historically speaking, every river in Britain was a Salmon river (I remember reading somewhere that Henry II, on being presented with a polar bear by his Royal Brother of Norway, kept it at the Tower of London, but let it out in the Thames on a long rope to find its own food—which, we may presume, consisted mainly of Salmon.) Can anything be done to stop pollution from banishing Salmon from one more river after another? Here again Dr. Jones, though by no means over-optimistic, has many wise and interesting things to say.

What is the explanation of the fact that a large fraction of male Salmon become sexually mature when still in the small parr stage, and may, as I mentioned earlier, achieve successful paternity even in the presence of a huge adult rival? We do not know for sure; but Dr. Jones suggests the probable explanation—that this precocious sexuality is a kind of insurance, making certain that more eggs will be fertilized than might otherwise be the case (for instance, if the big male of an adult pair were already more or less sexually spent).

Is it true that Salmon on their way back from the sea return to the same river which they descended as parr, one or several years previously? Here, Dr. Jones tells us, the answer is a qualified affirmative. Many, perhaps most of them do so, but not all. This of course prompts the further question, how do they find the "right" river? Dr. Jones gives a full account of the fascinating experiments and hypotheses on this subject, and concludes that each river has its own characteristic odour, due to the slightly different substances dissolved in its water, and the Salmon can recognise this particular smell even after several years' absence in the sea.

Salmon and their relatives—trout, char and the like—disclose many interesting facts about the evolution of species and races. When different assemblages of fish become isolated from each other in landlocked lakes or separate river-systems, they tend to diverge genetically. There are distinct subspecies of landlocked Salmon, and even of landlocked Salmon parr, and innumerable or at least very numerous varieties of white-fish (Coregonus) are found in different lakes, sometimes achieving sufficient distinctiveness to be given special local names, such as Gwyniad or Vendace. Various of them are on the interesting borderline between subspecies and full species.

If you like spectacular details, you will find some here. At one pool in Ross-shire, Salmon have been seen making a leap of 11 ft. 4 inches vertical, which requires a pre-leaping water-speed of over 20 m.p.h.

But the chief interest of Dr. Jones' book resides not in such details, however arresting, but in its careful marshalling of facts and evidence concerning the Salmon—a strange and splendid organism with a strange and wonderful life-history. Not least, the reader will discover how many problems are still unsolved, how many facts remain to be discovered. He will end up, we feel sure, with an enhanced respect for scientific naturalists like Dr. Jones who are helping us to understand the workings of evolution and the behaviour of its living products.

THE EDITORS

AUTHOR'S PREFACE

IT WAS with considerable trepidation that I accepted the publisher's invitation to write this book because the subject is so vast that no single person can cover it adequately. The present work therefore, is largely personal and consequently there are many of its aspects with which I have not dealt very fully.

I have tried to stress certain important matters, for example the dangerous consequences of continuing human depredations on our Salmon population. Most of all, I have tried to stress our ignorance of the *fundamental* biology of the Salmon. I feel that nothing less than a national laboratory can hope to tackle these problems adequately. Such an institution would need the full cooperation of River Boards, riparian owners, commercial fisheries, industrial concerns, anglers etc. Large scale long-term experiments are essential, they will be costly, yet I think sufficient money for such work *must* be made available if we are to preserve our Salmon.

I hope that this book will prove of interest to anglers and maybe show them that many of their problems are as yet unanswered. I am fully aware that I have dealt inadequately with the behaviour of the Salmon during its migration upstream—a subject of considerable interest to my many fishing friends in this country and in Norway. Unfortunately, despite the innumerable theories (often not based on fact), we know little about this part of the life of the Salmon. I am no angler, and have still to catch a Salmon on rod and line. But, I am very interested in the activities of anglers, and spend many hours discussing with them their views and problems. Even so, I feel it would be very presumptuous of me to include in this book a chapter on angling.

The arch enemy pollution merits a book to itself, as also do such matters as hydroelectric schemes, drainage, and other "essential" works. All I can do at this stage is ask that a competent *practical* biologist be consulted *before* the damage is done.

I am greatly indebted to the Editors, especially Sir Julian Huxley, F.R.S., for a great deal of advice and constructive criticism. I am very grateful to Professor R. J. Pumphrey, F.R.S., for reading the manuscript in detail and for long discussions which resulted in a great improvement in the presentation of the subject matter and the clarity of my English. I wish also to thank Miss J. Hughes for a great deal of valuable assistance in checking references, compiling the index, etc. I am indebted to Messrs. Irvine, Lee and Fleming for many of the excellent photographs, and finally I must thank Mrs. Richardson, Miss Silverstone and Mrs. Peat, who at various times have uncomplainingly typed and retyped the manuscript. I regret that I have not been able to include the more recent works of Hoar, Hasler and many others in this book.

J. W. JONES

CHAPTER I

THE KING OF FISH

'FOR many years past I have scarcely done anything else either officially or privately, except to attend to and carefully watch the interests of the King of Fish, the Salmon, the great *Salmo salar*.'' So wrote Frank Buckland in 1880. In making the same claim for myself in 1956, I can only repeat his complaint of the "difficulty in selecting from the mountain of information which exists on the subject of the Salmon . . ."

Since Buckland's time this mountain has grown high. Despite the fierce light which is said to beat upon a throne, much of the private life of the King of Fish still remains obscure; and even where the facts are well known, it is often impossible to find a reasonable interpretation of them.

Why can a fish, which *never* feeds in fresh water after it has come up from the sea, be taken on such lures as a bunch of worms, a prawn, a gaudy artificial "fly" and a spinner which imitates a small fish? This is perhaps the oldest of all the questions about the salmon. It remains unanswered.

The body of knowledge about the Atlantic Salmon, *Salmo salar*, now established is considerable; but I must emphasise not only our ignorance of some aspects of its life, but also the provisional and speculative nature of our conclusions about other aspects. In order to make this clear at the outset it is necessary forthwith to give an outline of its life history and genealogy. And, as it will be necessary very frequently to compare what we know of the Atlantic Salmon with what we know of other salmon, the former, *Salmo salar*, the Atlantic Salmon, *our* salmon, will thus always be written with a capital S, and other salmon with a small s, i.e. Salmon and salmon respectively.

For years the still unanswered questions about the Salmon have been argued in parliament and public house. The exposure of the secret life of the Salmon is scientific detection on a grand scale; and nearly everyone loves a good detective story: but this is big business as well as entertainment. Every year more than five million pounds of Salmon, much of it caught by licensed netsmen, is sold in Britain at more than ten shillings a pound. Large sums of money are locked up in fishing rights and fishing tackle and spent every year on rents, licences and permits. Although the annual turnover of the Salmon fishery in Britain may be little less than the fifteen million dollars yearly of the Pacific salmon industry of British Columbia, the days are long past when apprentices in Britain petitioned against being given Salmon to eat more than twice a week. The eating of Salmon in Great Britain is now a luxury and the pursuit of them with line and rod a sport for the well-to-do.

It is a good thing for all of us that there has been a powerful and vocal interest vested in the fishery. For more than 150 years the Salmon and his humbler cousin, the trout, have been the first indicators of the insidious pollution of our rivers. Unchecked, pollution puts an end to all angling and all life, and turns once clear waterways into open sewers like the Mersey, the Irwell, parts of the Trent and many others. In the long run the preservation of those of our rivers which are not yet polluted, and the reclamation of those that are, is much more important to each one of us than the particular preservation of the Salmon. But it is the sensitivity of the Salmon itself that has so often been the first inspirer of remedial action. The Salmon tolerates pollution scarcely at all. It is to save the Salmon that litigation, or the threat of it, has often stopped pollution before it had gone so far that reclamation became extremely difficult. It is the Salmon that has aroused public awareness of the dangers of pollution and touched the conscience of industry over the disposal of the wastes of trade.

In the shallow waters of streams, where the water is clean and the bottom is gravel, the Salmon's life-cycle begins. At about the end of March the fertilized eggs, which have been buried several inches deep by their mother, hatch; the young fish (*alevins*) which emerge into the water between the stones, have yolk-sacs attached to the under surface of their bodies; on this yolk they feed and develop in the gravel for some weeks, moving more freely as their yolk-sacs get smaller. Eventually the young Salmon make their way above the surface of the gravel. Their yolk-sacs disappear completely. Now they are called *fry*, or *fingerlings*, and are about one inch long: feeding and growing, they disperse.

I am not quite certain when a fingerling can properly be said to become a *parr*—the next stage in its life-cycle. Presumably it does so when it reaches a length greater than that of a man's finger. The change between these two stages is no more than a change in size. Two-year-old parr range from 4½ to 8 and rarely 10 inches in length. On either side of the body of these graceful fish "parr-marks" can be clearly seen as a series of eight to eleven dark blotches which look rather like thumb-prints and which only become eclipsed when the fish prepares for its migration to the sea (Fig. 1, p. 4). Until the middle of the nineteenth century it was thought that the parr was a species of fish distinct from the Salmon.

After a year or more in the fresh water of the river, the parr is ready to go to sea. On its scales a substance, *guanine,* has been deposited, hiding its parr-marks and giving it a shiny silvery appearance. It is now called a *smolt* (not to be confused with the smelt, which is a fish of the genus *Osmerus*).

Not all parr become smolts at the same age. The time of the transition varies with the geographical locations of the rivers which they inhabit. In general the farther north the river, the longer does the parr stay in that river before it becomes a smolt. In the Hampshire Avon I found that over ninety per cent of the smolts were migrating seawards in their second year—that is they were one-year-olds, or yearlings. But in the northernmost rivers of Scandinavia, the parr may be seven or even eight years old before they become smolts. In Great Britain the majority of young

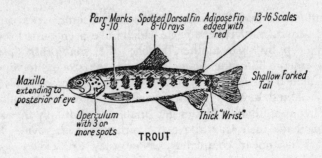

Fig. 1. The specific characters of young Salmon and trout of five to six inches in length

Salmon are two years old when they leave the rivers. Most of them do so in late March, April, or May. Where they migrate to, and for how long, are problems of special interest and depend on several factors which I shall discuss in Chapters 4 and 5, pp. 57 and 64.

We still know very little about the life of Salmon in the sea. Where do the smolts go? Do they all disappear into the unfished regions of the oceans, or do they, as is claimed by Huntsman (1939) for some of the Canadian Salmon, stay fairly near to the mouth of their parental stream or river? Why do they come back to the rivers to spawn, and what impels them to start this hazardous journey? Why do some come back after a comparatively short stay in the sea of only a year and a half, whereas others may stay for four years or maybe more? Do they really have a homing instinct? What part does their sense of smell play in their return journey? Do they return to the rivers in which they were born? To what extent is their behaviour hereditary;

does "like beget like", that is, do the progeny of fish which enter our rivers in spring also return in spring? The answers to such questions, so far as they are yet answerable, are the material of later chapters. All that can be said here is that the Salmon do eventually leave their excellent feeding grounds in the sea, start fasting as they reach our coasts, and continue to fast in fresh water. The urge which forces them to leave the feeding grounds must be a powerful one; for there is little doubt that while in the sea the Salmon feed very well indeed. The two-year-old smolt leaving the river may be merely five or six inches long and a few ounces in weight, yet after only a year of sea-feeding it may have increased in length to eighteen or twenty inches and in weight to three or more pounds. After four years in the sea the fish may weigh forty pounds: in Canada some Salmon of this age have weighed a hundred pounds or more.

Once they have reached the open sea, British and other European Salmon are seldom caught or seen. Salmon are, of course, caught in the sea by inshore fisheries; but there are very few records of Salmon caught in open water. It is possible that some are caught but are not reported; but such captures are certainly not common.

After a year or more in the sea, the adult Salmon make their way back to the rivers. They do not all return at the same time. In the Welsh Dee, for instance, some Salmon have been seen moving upstream as early as January, as well as in every other month of the year. This does not happen in all our rivers. Some rivers are "early" or spring-fish rivers; Salmon begin to arrive in large numbers in the Welsh Dee shortly before the fishing season opens on 15 March, and their run continues throughout spring, summer and early autumn. Other rivers such as the Cumberland Derwent have very few fish running upstream in spring; most of the Salmon in this river are caught in early summer and autumn. Such rivers are called summer-fish rivers. Finally there are rivers, often called late rivers, into which no Salmon run until late summer. Why Salmon rivers should differ so markedly is another unanswered question.

We know for certain that the incoming Salmon are returning

5

to the rivers in order to spawn, and that most of them will do so. To reach their spawning grounds, which are usually far from the river mouth, Salmon must ascend rapids, leap falls and risk a fatal encounter with the angler, the netsman, and the poacher. The upstream movement of the fish is often (in our better rivers) made a little easier by the presence of fish-passes or ladders on the more inaccessible falls and weirs.

Many picturesque accounts of the upstream journey have been published, and the spectacular leaping of Salmon at falls has often been exaggerated. However the truth is spectacular enough. In 1931 Calderwood described a leap of 11 feet 4 inches over a perpendicular fall on the River Orrin in Ross-shire. The height of the leap was measured from the water-level of the pool below to the water-level of the pool above; of the fish attempting it only about one in every twenty managed to get over. But the fact that Salmon can leap over eleven feet does not mean that smaller leaps are necessarily more easily made; small falls may often be unsurmountable because of the shallowness of the water below them. In such a leap as that described by Calderwood, the fish must have had a vertical speed of 20 m.p.h. as it left the water at the foot of the fall. The Salmon needs a good depth of water to gain momentum, and the general opinion is that this depth should be three times the height of the leap. It has been said that a leaping Salmon once out of the water propels itself through the air by flapping its tail, but this would be quite useless. In most of the leaps I have seen, the tail was not flapped sideways, and when I did observe tail-flapping it seemed to be an attempt by the fish to keep on an even keel (Plate 1, p. 16).

Once Salmon enter our rivers we know little more of their movements than we do of their movements in the sea, and our tentative conclusions are necessarily still based on non-scientific observations and often hearsay. We do not even know how fast Salmon move upstream—though we know a little about the conditions of the river which the Salmon find favourable for upstream movement. A great deal has still to be learned about the adult Salmon in the river; and the information can only be obtained by large-scale trapping and tagging of incoming fish.

By October and November, most of the Salmon are near, or on, their spawning places. At these places the river is shallow and has a clean gravel bottom. The fish which enter the river are such gleaming, well-proportioned, silvery creatures as would adorn a fishmonger's slab. By the time they are ready to spawn the males are reddish and quite hideous, with elongated jaws the lower of which is upcurved at its tip and fits into a socket in the upper; and the females are generally big-bellied and dark. At this stage the fish loiter for some time in the pools, occasionally above, more usually below the areas of spawning gravel. It is here, I think, that preliminary pairing takes place.

The courtship and spawning of the fish deserve a chapter to themselves (Chapter 6, p. 92). After it is over, the fish show clear signs of exhaustion. They are in poor condition, their bodies are thin, and often lacerated and covered with fungus. Most of these *kelts,* as they are now called, die before they reach the sea; and the few that survive are nearly all females. Why so many males die after spawning is another puzzling problem since, as will be seen later, the females appear to expend a great deal of energy in preparing the bed in the gravel in which the eggs are laid, while the males are having a comparatively restful time on guard. Meanwhile, the fertilized eggs are developing in the bed so carefully made by the female and the cycle is complete. The kelts that reach the sea start feeding again, and in the course of time such of them as escape their enemies in the sea, will once again leave their marine feeding pastures to undertake another spawning journey.

An understanding of the status and habits of our North Atlantic Salmon is impossible without some outline of the group of fishes to which it belongs—and without some comparison with other members of the group. The rest of this chapter is therefore devoted to an outline of some of the more important details of the Salmon's place in the natural classification and of its relationship with some of its cousins.

The Salmon is a member of the family Salmonidae, which is a subdivision of the sub-order Salmonoidei. Other members of this sub-order found in Britain are the Thymallidae (Graylings), the Osmeridae (Smelts), and the Argentinidae (the Argentines). The families Bathylagidae, Microstomidae and Xenopthalmichthyidae are deep-sea Salmonoidei, the Salangidae are shore-fishes of Eastern Asia which enter rivers, the Retropinnidae are found in Australia and New Zealand, and the Hoplochitonidae are found in the South Pacific (S. America, Falkland Is., S. Australia, Tasmania and New Zealand). There is only one species in the family Plecoglossidae: this enters the rivers of Korea, Japan and China.

The family Salmonidae is nowadays (Berg, 1932-33) divided into two sub-families. 1, Salmonini which includes the genera *Salmo* (Salmon and Trout), *Salvelinus* (Chars), *Oncorhynchus* (the Pacific salmon), *Hucho, Cristivomer, Salmothymus:* 2, Coregonini— the white fish—which includes the genera *Stenodus* and *Coregonus.*

Salmon and their allies have a striking superficial resemblance to the herrings, but they are distinguished from them—among other differences—by their practice of laying relatively large eggs in fresh water. (Fig. 2 shows the distribution of the species *Salmo salar* and of the genus *Oncorhynchus*). The genus *Coregonus* includes a number of species which are the basis of important lake fisheries in North America and Europe, and a number of varieties dubiously entitled to specific rank and peculiar to different lakes in Britain where they have been given local names: Gwyniad, Pollan, Powan, Vendace. Near the northern limits of the genus *Coregonus,* many of its species are *anadromous* like the Salmon, i.e. after an early development in fresh water, they go down to the sea to feed and grow and return later to rivers and lakes to lay their eggs.

The genus *Salmo* contains a number of species besides *S. salar,* the Atlantic Salmon, which is the hero of this book, and to some of these I shall have to refer often. *Salmo trutta* is our trout, and includes both the anadromous sea-trout and the fresh-water brown trout. It is widespread in Europe and Western Asia as far East as Afghanistan, and in the rivers of Northern and Western coasts of Europe from the White Sea to North Africa. *Salmo irideus,* the rainbow-trout, now generally known in its native country as *S. gairdnerii,* plays in N. America west of the Mississippi the same role as *S. trutta* in Europe. (Nowadays two forms of *S. gairdnerii* are recognised, the fresh-water Rainbow and the

8

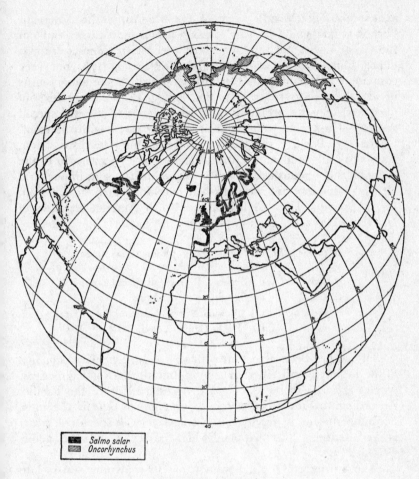

Salmo salar
Oncorhynchus

Fig. 2. Distribution of the species *S. salar* and the genus *Oncorhynchus* (approximate)

anadromous Steelhead). East of the Mississippi the American "brook-trout" is a Char, *Salvelinus fontinalis*, and the "trout" of the Great Lakes and the "sea-trout" of Eastern Canada are also char. Our British char are purely fresh-water fish, not very common, and patchy in their distribution. Some taxonomists divide them into several species, but (like our "species" of *Coregonus*) they are probably all relict varieties of one widespread species. They seem to be fighting a losing battle with the trout.

In the Pacific, the salmon corresponding in distribution, habits and place in nature to the single species *Salmo salar* of the Atlantic is the genus *Oncorhynchus*. *Oncorhynchus* is split into several clearly defined species, some of which overlap in their distribution. (See Appendix II). A list of the North American species of *Oncorhynchus* is as follows:—

a.	*O. tschawytscha*	the Spring, King, Quinnat, Sacramento, Columbia River, Tyee, or Chinook salmon;
b.	*O. nerka*	the Sockeye, Red, or Blueback salmon;*
c.	*O. kisutch*	the Silver or Coho salmon;
d.	*O. gorbuscha*	the Humpback or Pink salmon;
e.	*O. keta*	the Dog or Chum salmon.

I have not been able to obtain very comprehensive accounts of the Japanese and Siberian salmon, but all the North American species are also to be found on the western side of the Pacific. According to Starr Jordan (1925) *Oncorhynchus keta* is the most abundant species in Japan, and a non-American species *O. masou* is also found. (See Appendix II for a key to the genus *Oncorhynchus*).

The Spring or Quinnat salmon has its spawning run in late spring and early summer, and may travel as much as 2,000 miles up the Yukon to spawn. The young may either go to sea during their first year of life, or may remain one or even two years in the stream. These fish grow rapidly in the sea, and mature in three to eight years, generally in four or five: at maturity they

---

* Now known as *O. nerka nerka* to distinguish it from the non-migratory subspecies the Kokanee (*Oncorhynchus nerka kennerlyi*).

generally weigh from 10 to 50 lb., but weights up to 108 lb. have been recorded.

The Sockeye salmon migrate upstream mainly in the spring and early summer: and the adults only enter rivers fed by lakes, through which they pass to spawn in the tributary streams running into the lakes; they may migrate distances of nearly 2,000 miles upstream. After hatching the following spring, the young descend into the lakes—where they spend usually one, sometimes two, and occasionally three years before going down to the sea. Some may move to sea as fry. The Sockeye usually matures at four or five years of age, though some may not do so until they are six, seven, or very rarely eight years old. The weight at maturity is usually 5 to 7 lb., but fish of up to 15½ lb. have been taken.

The Coho or Silver salmon may spawn at short distances from the sea, but in larger rivers may move up to the upper tributaries. The great majority of the young remain one year in fresh water, but a few migrate to sea in their second and third years of river life. In the sea, growth is rapid and maturity is attained at the end of the third summer; the Coho's usual weight at maturity is from 6 to 12 lb., but weights of up to 26½ lb. have been recorded.

The Pink or Humpback salmon usually do not go very far from tidal water, but may occasionally travel upstream for considerable distances—for example, the 200 miles from the sea to Babine Lake on the upper reaches of the Skeene River in British Columbia. At spawning times the males develop very large humps on their backs—hence the name Humpback. The young go to sea as fry and attain maturity in two years, when their weight is usually between 3 and 5 lb., but fish weighing 10 lb. have been recorded.

The Chum or Dog salmon is a late runner, arriving in the rivers in autumn. It also generally spawns near the tidal waters; though some travel far upstream. The young have slender parr-marks, and go to sea soon after hatching. The fish generally attain maturity in their fourth year, when they usually weigh from 8 to 18 lb., but weights of 30 lb. have been recorded (for further details see Jordan, 1925, Haig-Brown, 1952).

The salmon family has long been the object of curiosity and

speculation among zoologists. Most particularly the three genera *Coregonus*, *Oncorhynchus* and *Salmo* have been studied, for all contain migratory as well as non-migratory forms.

Where and when did the *Salmonidae* originate? How did its members attain their present distribution? Was the common ancestor of the family exclusively a marine fish or exclusively a fresh-water fish? When did the ancestor of the salmon first begin to show the migratory habits exhibited by so many of its descendants of the present day?

In 1939 Tchernavin reviewed the problem and decided firmly in favour of a fresh-water origin. He found that in every genus of the family an exclusively fresh-water species was present, some genera being wholly fresh-water. He also found that "with few exceptions each migratory form has a close parallel fresh-water one," and pointed out that no member of the salmon family can breed in the sea. His summary of the biological evidence in favour of a fresh-water origin for the Atlantic Salmon in particular may be summarised as follows:—

i. the fish spawn in fresh water, overcome obstacles to reach their spawning grounds and thereby get as far away as possible from the sea;

ii. conditions suitable for spawning are only found in fresh water, that is, well-oxygenated flowing water;

iii. the specific gravity of the Salmon egg is less than that of sea-water, and it would float if fish spawned in the sea;

iv. artificial fertilization of the eggs of the Atlantic Salmon in sea-water has proved impossible;

v. young newly-hatched Salmon are intolerant of sea-water;

vi. sea-water is not necessary for the maturing of migratory *Salmonidae*: this is shown clearly by the development of testes in about 70 per cent of the male Atlantic Salmon parr.

The male parr of some Pacific salmon also attain maturity; there are two distinct types of male parr of the Japanese salmon (*Oncorhynchus masou*); one becomes sexually mature at the age of two years and stays in the river throughout its life, and the other migrates as a smolt in the normal manner to the sea.

Since Tchernavin's death some of his arguments have lost part of their force from the discovery that one species of Pacific salmon (*Oncorhynchus gorbuscha*) can spawn in estuaries where the water, if not as salt as the open sea, is at high tide strongly brackish. Hanavan and Skud (1954) have investigated the circumstances and find that many of the nests made in the gravel of the intertidal zone are covered with salt water for a substantial part of the autumn and winter incubation period. By using screened enclosures, Hanavan was able to show that the survival-rates of fish spawned in intertidal and in fresh water were comparable; his colleague Skud found that the salt-content of the water within the gravel of the spawning beds depends on the salinity of the overlying waters. At full tide, therefore, the salinity of the water around the eggs was apparently two-thirds that of the open ocean, but during the ebb tide the eggs were washed relatively free of salt water. It is thus apparent that the developing eggs withstand a considerable change of salinity. Are these intertidal spawners still in the process of establishing themselves as fully fresh-water forms, or are they moving back to a marine habitat?

The *Salmonidae* have no fossil history until relatively recent times. The only "Salmonid" known before the Pleistocene is probably a smelt, and the Pleistocene fossils are fragmentary and not very helpful. It is generally agreed that the family must have attained its present distribution during and partly as a result of the succession of ice-ages in Pleistocene and recent times, and that the genera *Salmo*, *Salvelinus* and *Oncorhynchus* arose from a common ancestor not later than the beginning of the Pleistocene, over half a million years ago. These three genera subsequently split into their present-day species in consequence of temporary geographical barriers to interbreeding, due to the advance and retreat of the ice-sheets and changes in the temperature of the seas.

We do not know whether the common ancestor was of marine or fresh-water origin: it might have been estuarine. It is the migratory habit which characterises the group and only the migratory habit can plausibly account for its circumpolar distribution. Migratory *Salmonidae* are found wherever in the northern hemisphere streams and lakes, which are not too completely ice-bound, give access to cool (and richly productive) seas. At the southern limits, Formosa, Southern California, North Africa, only fresh-water forms occur, presumably because the seas are now too warm to permit migration in these latitudes; but it must surely be presumed that these countries were originally populated by migrants during the last ice-age.

In 1930 Julian Huxley suggested, "that the trout is an animal which, though somatically [that is, in this context, as regards its general bodily maintenance] fully adapted to fresh-water life, is very imperfectly so adapted in its reproduction, its sperms being many times more efficient in a medium intermediate between its present and its ancestral environment."

In 1938 we followed up Huxley's suggestion by making observations on the activity of the sperm of adult Salmon and of parr in river water and in various dilutions of sea-water and also the sugar sucrose.

Almost immediately they were put in river water both types of spermatozoa became inactive; that is, they stopped swimming almost immediately. In various dilutions of sea-water they remained active for a greater length of time: in a 20 per cent dilution of sea-water they lasted for several minutes.

It was now necessary to find whether the activating influence of sea-water was primarily ionic or primarily osmotic. On the face of it it appeared that Salmon sperm must be adapted to an osmotic pressure equal to that of a one-in-five dilution of sea-water; but it did not follow that the activating influence of sea-water was entirely osmotic, that is, due to the penetration of substances from solution in the sea-water through the cell-membrane of the spermatozoa.

W. G. Ellis and I (1939) therefore tried to find the effect of a non-electrolyte on the sperm. As sea-water is a mixture of electrolytes and as its activating influence upon the sperm might have been ionic, this was a necessary control experiment to perform. We chose sucrose as the solute for our experiments, making the solutions with the same osmotic pressure as the various dilutions of sea-water previously used. The sperm behaved very much the same as they did in sea-water, suggesting that the activating influence in both tests was, indeed, osmotic.

Huxley's view that the sperm of trout are more efficient in a salinity intermediate between fresh water and that of the sea, can be taken therefore as equally applicable to the sperm of Salmon. But his inference that neither Salmon nor trout is very perfectly adapted to fresh-water life in its reproduction cannot be substantiated. The proof of the pudding is in the eating; and counts of eggs in the bed after normal spawning have shown that 90 to 100 per cent of Salmon eggs and of trout eggs have been fertilised and are developing.

All British Salmon spend part of their life in the sea, but in other parts of the world permanent fresh-water colonies of Salmon exist. In Lake Wener in Sweden, for example, the Salmon are non-migratory and attain an average weight of 8 lb., as do similar forms found in Lake Ladoga on the borders of Finland and Russia. Dwarfed forms, called *blege*, which do not reach a weight of more than half a pound, are found in southern Norway in Byglands Fiord Lake, in the Namsen river and also the River Otha (Dahl, 1928). In this river, Dahl estimated that the non-migratory habit was acquired about 9,000 years ago.

Several lakes in parts of Canada and the eastern United States have similar fresh-water colonies of fish generally regarded as sub-species of *Salmo salar* which have been called land-locked Salmon, though their access to the sea is not barred in all cases; this would indicate that these fish have evolved a fully fresh-water mode of existence for some reason other than physical inability to reach the sea.

The well-known non-migratory North American salmon, the Kokanee (*Oncorhynchus nerka kennerlyi*), is visually almost indis-tinguishable from the migratory Sockeye (*Oncorhynchus nerka nerka*), the only difference being that of size—except at maturity, when there is a difference in breeding colour and time of spawn-ing. It is probable, as suggested by Ricker (1938), that these two forms have evolved from a common stock in quite recent times. The Kokanee do not leave Cultus Lake. An intermediate form, the so-called "residual Sockeye" of Cultus Lake, is said to be the non-migratory progeny of the normal migratory Sockeye; these fish stay in the lake, but their progeny may or may not migrate seawards. These "residual Sockeye" spawn at least three weeks later than the Kokanees, so that interbreeding is negligible if it occurs at all.

In discussing the "land-locking" of salmon, Ward (1932) denies previous suggestions that either mechanical barriers or wealth of food-supply are effective factors: and it is certainly doubtful if any natural barrier short of complete interruption of the outflow could prohibit *downstream* migration for any length of time. He concluded, on the basis of a study of young Sockeye in Baker Lake in the State of Washington, that the ruling factor was temperature. Here a power-dam was erected at Concrete, forming a reservoir called Lake Shannon. Normally the young Sockeye moving seawards will, on entering a lake, swim along its shores till they come to an outlet; in Lake Shannon in summer the water-level is low and there is no outlet from the reservoir; moreover the surface waters are warm, and Ward believes that the young fish, temporarily unable to get out and repelled by the warm water, move down into the deeper part of the reservoir and here lose their urge to migrate. Ward then applies this argument to salmon in lakes of natural origin, and concludes that the land-locked salmon were held back not by the formation of a permanent mechanical barrier, but by some factors (such as temperature and water-level in the lake itself) which limited the movements of the young fish until in time they lost the urge to migrate to the sea. It will be interesting to see whether the construction of dams on some of our Scottish rivers will result in the production of land-locked forms.

The Salmon is found on both sides of the Atlantic from Massachusetts to Labrador on the west, through Greenland and Iceland to Scandinavia and the White Sea, in the Baltic and North Seas, the British Isles, North Germany, the Netherlands, France, the north of Spain and Portugal. The Salmon does not

Plate 1 (*opposite*)
Salmon leaping. (*Ronald Thompson*)

live in the Mediterranean, though it is said to have done so in the past. In Yugoslavia there is to be found the so-called Dalmatian salmon (*Salmo obtusirostris*), a small non-migratory fish which stays in fresh water throughout its life, looking very like a Salmon parr about ten to twelve inches in length. It can be distinguished from a parr by its small mouth and numerous gill-rakers. Tate Regan (1920) believes that this Dalmatian salmon is descended from Salmon parr which were tempted by the great abundance of caddis-flies in the river to remain there instead of going down to the sea. *Salmo obtusirostris* is, to quote Regan's words, "a witness of the former presence of salmon in the Mediterranean."

Tate Regan also suggested that there might be a lake-locked colony of non-migratory parr in Lough Conn (Eire, Co. Mayo). He has described one four-year parr from this lough which was twelve inches in length, and claims that others of this size have been seen. Such a colony may exist, but I should be happier if the evidence were stronger. Size alone cannot, in my opinion, be indicative of a non-migratory habit, otherwise one would expect the large Salmon parr I received from the River Teme to be non-migratory—they were almost twice as big as those from some smaller Welsh streams, yet these Teme fish migrate. Until we have proof of sexual maturity (in both sexes) it is wiser to assume that all our British Salmon parr eventually migrate to the sea.

To sum up, the *Salmonidae* is a family, of origin relatively recent in the geological sense, which is still in the process of active evolution. The common ancestor was a fish which utilised fresh waters as a safe if rather sterile nursery for its young, but which grew to maturity in highly productive temperate-to-cold seas. Tchernavin's argument that the ancestor was a fresh-water fish, because the fresh-water forms of today are "more primitive" than the migratory, cannot be sustained. It fails to explain the present-day distribution and it seems to be contrary to the facts observable in the case of *Salmo salar*. For the migratory Atlantic Salmon is a single interbreeding and remarkably homogeneous

---

Plate 2 (*opposite*)
A 42½lb cock salmon caught in the Hampshire Avon. (*John Tarlton*)

species round the enormous periphery of the North Atlantic: it is only where it is or has been cut off from migration that distinguishable specific or sub-specific groups have been evolved. In the Pacific the process has gone further, and *Oncorhynchus* is already split into well-marked species, which in turn are producing different subspecies as a consequence of land-locking. Perhaps evolution in the Atlantic basin has lagged one glacial period behind that in the Pacific.

CHAPTER 2

YOUNG SALMON IN THE RIVER

Alevins, Fry, Parr and Smolts

THE female Salmon is a good mother: she takes great pains in digging and shaping her nest in the river bed, and at the bottom of it she lays her eggs in November or December. She then covers them with gravel so that the young Salmon, when they hatch about 100 days later, may be twelve inches deep in it if the mother was large. Even a small fish of 4 or 5 lb. makes a bed six or eight inches deep. In a good spawning bed there is an adequate flow of water through the gravel at this depth: and it is a safe place for them, for they are very helpless at first. On emerging from the egg they are only about half an inch long, and the large yolk-sac attached to their bellies hinders movement. For three or four weeks after hatching, they live only on the yolk in their yolk-sacs, which gradually get smaller as they get bigger, and they move about very little. Stuart, (1953) who has carefully observed the development of young trout in their gravel nests, has found that the larvae of stone-flies and other predators which eat eggs and alevins, are usually only present in the top two inches of gravel. Stuart also investigated, in the laboratory, the response of young trout to light. For three days after hatching they are nearly motionless, then there is a long period, lasting until the yolk-sac is nearly absorbed, in which they swim actively away from light towards darkness. There follows a sudden and transient period of half an hour or so in which they swim towards light. After this the dominant factor in their orientation is no longer the direction of incident light, but the direction of the water-current. It is very tempting to associate the negative and positive responses to light respectively with the checking of migration into the top layer of gravel where predators lurk until the yolk-sac is absorbed, and with the hastening of migration through this danger zone when the time has come to emerge from the gravel. But too much emphasis should not yet be placed on the collation of laboratory and field observations. Danger is a relative matter, and trout and Salmon fry will continue for a long while, after first emerging from the gravel, to take refuge in it from disturbances in the water above.

At an age when they should still be in the gravel the young fish, (usually called alevins until the yolk-sac has been absorbed), will start to feed in laboratory conditions; and Stuart has observed that they will only take food, either living or dead, which is in motion, and that even at this early stage they seem able to distinguish colours. Many of his observations were made on young Salmon, as well as on trout; and up to this stage, the behaviour of both species seems very similar—except that Salmon eggs are generally buried deeper and in coarser gravel than trout eggs. But Stuart does point out some differences in the behaviour of young Salmon and young trout. For instance, on emergence from the gravel, Salmon fry are gregarious and tend to remain together in shoal formation; whereas young trout fry tend to disperse individually soon after emergence. (Plate 3a (p. 32) shows a newly hatched alevin, and also an egg containing an unhatched fish).

Salmon fry (or fingerlings) are generally visible on the surface of the gravel in early May, though the time of their emergence varies with the severity of the season and with the geographical position of the river. In colder waters development is considerably slower: in a hatchery, Salmon eggs which will hatch out in 90 days when the water temperature is 45°F, take 114 days at 36°F. When the young fish emerge, they are generally scaleless. Scales usually first appear when the fish are rather more than an inch in length. Their rudiments are to be seen at first along the lateral line, as a series of small papillae; more will be said about them in the next chapter (p. 43).

Salmon larger than a man's finger are commonly called parr,

but they have a variety of local names—pink, samlet, peal, branlin, skegger, locksper, skirling, laspring, samson, and (in Wales) sil. They are recognisable by a series of dark shadowy blotches along each side of the body which look somewhat like thumb-prints; these "parr-marks" are also visible, though usually less conspicuous, in young trout, with which Salmon parr are often confused (see Appendix 1, p. 154 and Fig. 1, p. 4).

It is not so very long ago that parr were regarded as quite unrelated to adult Salmon. In 1807 Turton, in his *British Fauna*, expressed his belief that the parr which he called *Salmo salmulus* (Ray) was a distinct species, and Sir Humphrey Davy in his book, *Salmonia* (1832), considered parr to be the hybrid offspring of Salmon and trout. On the other hand, Stoddart claimed definitely in the *Scottish Angler* of 1831 that parr were the young of Salmon.

It was not until Shaw's classical experiments of 1836 and 1837 that the eggs of Salmon were artificially fertilized with adult Salmon sperm and the young were reared. And Shaw (1840) first proved that the progeny of such a fertilization were indistinguishable from Salmon parr in the rivers.

Throughout its life in the river, the parr has to contend with many enemies, of which man is now perhaps the worst. A great number of parr are destroyed yearly by fishermen, and many others are killed by pollution, to which they are even less resistant than full-grown Salmon and far less so than coarse fish. Other animals considered, rightly or wrongly, to be enemies of Salmon fry and parr are trout, pike, chub, perch, eels, cormorants, ducks, swans and herons.

An interesting experiment in the reduction of predation was carried out in Cultus Lake (British Columbia). The squawfish (*Ptychocheilus oregonensis*) habitually eats Sockeye salmon less than one year old, the usual number of fry found in its stomach being three; the char (*Salvelinus malma*) eats young Sockeye and other fishes, and in May and June destroys almost as many as does the trout. The greatest number found in one char stomach was 93, and the average was 11. Unlike the squawfish, the trout eats young Sockeye throughout the year, and very little else in May and early June when the fry are emerging from the gravel. By gill-netting, Foerster and Ricker (1940) reduced the squawfish and char to about one-tenth of their original numbers (the trout population was reduced to a lesser extent). As a result of this, the survival rate of the young salmon was, in three years, increased about three-and-a-third times; Foerster and Ricker reckon that this, in Cultus Lake, has resulted in the saving of about 380,000 Sockeye salmon, a very striking figure (see also Ricker, 1941). It would be interesting to carry out a similar experiment in this country.

In Sweden, Hult and Johnels (1949) tried to determine the loss due to predators, of Atlantic Salmon fry during the first twenty-four hours after they had been planted in the river. Before the fry were planted some of the fish were trapped and an estimate of the fish population made. 176 perch were caught, marked and returned to the river with considerably smaller numbers of other fish—8 pike (*Esox lucius*), 6 ruff (*Acerina cernua*), 12 roach (*Rutilus rutilus*), 2 rudd (*Scardinius eryophthalmus*) and 13 bream (*Abramis brama*). About 30,000 Salmon fry were planted in the area of river where the trapping had been carried out, at a density of about two per square metre. As was expected, some could be seen in the water after planting. The fish predators were trapped, and removed daily from the traps; of the 176 perch (*Perca fluviatilis*) which had been marked in the area, 16 were recaptured within three days. From an estimate of total perch in the river area, it was calculated that if all the perch had been eating like the captured ones, about 11 per cent of the total Salmon fry planted would have been eaten by the perch population in twenty-four hours. But the authors point out that as the perch were spawning at the time of the experiment, and were probably not feeding with their usual rapacity, this figure is very likely an under-estimate. Of the other fish present, the ruff, the roach and the pike had all eaten Salmon fry, and in another experiment the chub (*Leuciscus cephalus*) was found to feed on them voraciously. This experiment confirms that young Salmon have many enemies, but I should like to see it repeated differently: instead of planting fry I would plant eggs in the gravel so that the fry would hatch out normally and get used to their environment before having to contend with predators.

Some birds are also reputed to be enemies of young Salmon. In Canada, Huntsman (1941) reduced, as far as possible (for one year), the numbers of fish-eating birds (belted kingfishers and mergansers*) on a selected stream, with the result that the number of descending smolts in this stream was more than doubled. The smolts were marked and their increased migration was later reflected in the catches of adult fish. It would be of considerable interest if a similar experiment could be carried out in this country where the predators which need investigation are:—cormorant, shag, heron, and, certainly less important, gulls, which probably only feed on the migrating smolts. It is, of course, necessary that any such investigation should be a small-scale pilot experiment on water so chosen that control-comparison is possible and the results can be taken seriously. The indiscriminate slaughter of alleged predators has too often, in the past, resulted from ignorance and prejudice, or been a cover for inefficient management. It is certainly not justified in this country on any evidence yet available.

It has often been said that teal, mallard, and swans are enemies of Salmon as they are supposed to uproot spawning beds and eat the fertilized eggs and fry. Berry (1933-34) described how he saw swans, teal and mallard poking their bills amongst the stones where Salmon had spawned. He believed that the swans were quite definitely uprooting the redds, but he did not know whether it was for ova or some other food. After observing so many Salmon spawnings, I do not think that any bird could uproot a Salmon redd: the eggs of each spawning occupy a comparatively small area, and there is little indication from above of their exact position, so that uprooting would be a very chancy business for the bird; it would require the displacement of a large

* It is of interest that White (1957) reports that almost 1,200 American mergansers were shot on the Miramichi River, in Canada. 86% of these birds had been eating young Salmon. From his figures White estimated the annual consumption of these 1,200 birds to be 1,900,000 Salmon parr.

amount of gravel to secure a good feed of eggs. It is much more likely that these birds were looking for stray eggs, of which there may be an appreciable percentage in some redds. (See Chapter 6, p. 92).

Even the tiny dipper has been accused of robbing spawning-beds. This is manifestly absurd, for the fertile eggs are under gravel which so small a bird is quite incapable of displacing. Nevertheless, dippers are very fond of Salmon eggs, and we were able to entice one into our Salmon observation tank at Pont-Barcer, near Corwen, N. Wales, by placing eggs on the wall, on the rocks in the tank above water, and eventually underwater on the gravel. Soon the dipper was tempted into the fast-flowing stream, and I have been lucky enough to enjoy the rare sight of it swimming underwater on five or six occasions. The bird uses its wings to propel itself against the current; when it is below the surface its whole body shines like silver owing to the air trapped in its feathers—a wonderful sight. I took a ciné film of one of these underwater excursions; in this instance the bird swam underwater for about a foot at an angle of about 70° to the surface; as soon as it touched the gravel with its beak it stopped flapping its wings and was carried back to the surface almost to the spot from which it started. Several of these downward darts were filmed and it seemed certain that the bird was prodding around for the stray Salmon eggs which we had set out for it. On one other visit the bird swam about six feet against the current; it moved upstream apparently without effort, its head moving from side to side as it searched for food. I never saw the dipper walk on the bottom as apparently it frequently does in stiller water; it may be that the water flow in the tank was too great to allow this (Jones and King, 1952). I must repeat that the dipper does no harm to our Salmon fisheries. The cleaning up of the very small percentage of stray eggs which are probably not fertilized, which are certainly not going to complete their development and which, if not eaten by the dipper or another scavenger, will be a substrate for fungus, is a sanitary measure which fishery managers should welcome.

Salmon parr cannot withstand very high temperatures and

will all die if the temperature rises to between 32°C and 34°C (Huntsman, 1942). This may happen when large volumes of condenser-water are passed into a Salmon river, or, more rarely, when there is a drought followed by a heat-wave. Brett (1952, 1956) found that the ultimate lethal temperatures for Pacific salmon of about 5 cm. in length varied as follows:— Spring, 25·1°C; Coho, 25·0°C; Sockeye, 24·4°C; Pink, 23·9°C; and Chum, 23·8°C; they are apparently less resistant to high temperatures than the Atlantic salmon.

The feeding habits of Salmon parr were studied by Carpenter (1940). She found that in the Welsh Dee they were indiscriminately carnivorous, and that their diet varied in close accord with the number and relative accessibility of the species of food present in the river. In autumn the fish ate quite a lot of leaf-eating insects which at that season of the year fell into the rivers as the leaves decayed. A marked seasonal cycle in feeding was observed, which seemed to be directly dependent on the life-histories of the various food-organisms. Carpenter found no evidence of a seasonal loss of appetite: when the fish were not feeding it was because food was not available. Allen (1940, 1941) also found that the feeding of the parr was determined largely by what was available to them, though there was some evidence that they did, to a very small extent, select their food. The parr of the Eden and Thurso studied by Allen appeared to feed most actively in May and April: towards the later part of the summer feeding slowed down. As a result of this feeding cycle, growth was most rapid in the early part of the summer, slowed down in July and August and stopped from September until March or April. He was unfortunately not able to catch any parr in the winter. Allen seems to have concluded that in the rivers he examined, parr do not feed at a temperature below 7°C. According to him, below this temperature the parr remain quiet in deep pools, feed little or not at all, and do not grow. I am not at all certain that these statements are justified; the fact that he could not catch the parr does not necessarily mean that they were lying quiet and not feeding, even if they were in the pools (where I am certain their behaviour could not be observed). I have sometimes seen Salmon parr feeding actively when the temperature of the water was barely 1°C, and frequently when it has been 4°C or 5°C. These observations were made in the Salmon observation-tank which will be described in detail later (p. 97).

Carpenter (1940) examined the stomachs of small samples of parr of approximately the same size taken in all the winter months except November from the Welsh Dee and tributaries; and in no instance was the stomach empty. She measured the volume of the food in cubic centimetres: the following figures for parr from the River Ceiriog show that the volume of food present in February, for instance, was almost as great as that in May.

Month	Average volume of food in cc.	Month	Average volume of food in cc.
July	2·55	January	0·52
August	negligible	February	2·20
September	1·86	March	1·90
October	0·65	April	2·01
November	—	May	2·49
December	0·35	June	1·45
		July	1·59

(From Carpenter Text figure 2, page 87).

Of course, such results do not give the full picture: one ought to be certain that the fish taken in the samples were at all times at "the same course of their meal", and of Carpenter's fish some may have just started feeding and others may have been near repletion. Moreover, a full stomach is no final indication of the *rate* at which food is being taken, since the digestive process is certainly slowed down at low temperatures. Nevertheless, it is of some significance that there was quite a lot of food in the stomachs in the winter months. I am certain that some growth does take place through-out winter in the parr of the Welsh Dee. Growth-rings are produced on the scales throughout this period (Chapter 3, p. 43) and there is some evidence, as shown in Figure 3, p. 27, that there is a general increase in length (Jones, 1949).

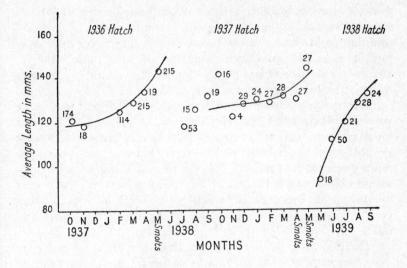

FIG. 3. The average lengths of each monthly sample of Welsh Dee Salmon parr and smolts hatched in 1936, 1937, 1938 plotted against time of capture. Curves freely drawn; figures at each point represent the number of fish in each sample

A very interesting series of observations on the diurnal feeding habits of young Atlantic Salmon and young "trout" (*Salvelinus fontinalis*) in captivity was made by Hoar (1942); the fish take little food from about 10.00 p.m. to 5.00 a.m. and he presumes they tend to "sleep" in the hours of darkness. But the fish can and will feed in the dark on occasion; this he showed experimentally by keeping them in a light-proof box. Strong sunlight depresses their feeding, as does high temperature (25°C to 27°C)—which at first slows down feeding and then brings it to a complete stop. After being subjected to high temperature a fish will not feed again until it has had time to recover at lower temperature. Young Salmon feed with less intensity from one to two hours after sunset to about two or three hours after sunrise; and feeding is frequently slowed down in the middle of the day; this is primarily due to rising temperature, although strong light is a

27

possible associated factor. Other workers have found that Salmon tend to avoid strong light by keeping in deeper waters at midday, and that trout rise for insect larvae mainly during the periods of low light-intensity in the morning and evening (van Someren, 1940). Yet McKenzie (1935) found that changes in light intensity had no effect on the feeding of cod.

Some people believe that during their river-life parr may move considerable distances, and Huntsman and others in Canada have found parr stranded on beaches, and concluded that a considerable proportion of the parr in nearby rivers move regularly into the estuary or even into the sea. My own belief, unsupported by any substantial evidence, is that, in this country at least, parr tend to stay near the area in which they were hatched, and that none get into the sea except by an accident which is inevitably fatal.

There is little doubt, however, that ripe male Salmon parr (see Chapter 7, p. 117) migrate upstream just before and during the spawning season. At the experimental observation-tank on the Alwen over the period 1946-1954, we have every year observed this upstream migration, which has enabled us to catch ripe male Salmon parr for our tank experiments. The parr we caught had migrated up the small stream-like overflow, which is about a foot wide and six inches deep and about seven yards long, and runs out of the observation-tank parallel with the main stream into which it empties. This upstream migration takes place periodically, and the fish are easily captured by placing a net across the stream at its entry into the main river and turning off the water-supply to the tank. It was only very rarely that female parr or unripe male parr were caught in this manner. The upstream migration did not appear to be related to temperature; on the other hand, we believe that the fish moved up after a spate, as is indicated in the following table which shows capture of parr at the overflow from the tank in 1948. I should add that this migration may only have amounted to a journey of about a mile upstream to nearby spawning beds, though there is no way of telling how far upstream the parr had come before they were trapped.

Date	State of River	No. of Parr caught
Nov. 9–12	Low	0
Nov. 13–14	Flood	71
Nov. 15–22	Very high flood, no netting possible	0
Nov. 23–Dec. 2	Falling	0
Dec. 3	Rising	3
Dec. 4–6	Falling	0
Dec. 7	Small flood	0
Dec. 8–9	No data	0
Dec. 10	Flood	4
Dec. 11	Slight rise	0
Dec. 12	Falling	1
Dec. 13	Rising	0
Dec. 14	Falling	0
Dec. 15	Falling	0

TABLE 1. Number of ripe male Salmon parr caught at the observation tank in 1948. (Three of the 71 fish caught on November 13-14 were females).

The length of time the young Salmon spend in the river before starting their seaward migration as smolts varies with the geographical location of the river. Generally the further north the river the older the smolts at migration. In the Hampshire Avon I found that over 90 per cent of the smolts were yearlings, that is, were in the second summer of their life (Jones, 1950), but in the Welsh Dee and Cumberland Derwent, for instance, over 90 per cent migrated as two-year-olds, and were in the third summer of their life: a few migrated as yearlings, and a few as three-year-olds (Jones, 1953). Among the more northerly Scottish rivers, the Grimersta (Lewis) was found by Menzies (1926) to have over 60 per cent of its smolts moving seawards as three-year-olds. In some of the more northerly Scandinavian rivers, the parr stay in the river for seven or eight years before going down to the sea. It is more than likely that this differential migration is related to temperature, day-length and feeding, and that it affects the subsequent growth-rate of the fishes. This variation in the age of Salmon on their first seaward migration has been used as a basis for conjecture about the cause of the urge which drives them to the sea. Many workers have shown, from scale examination and the estimation of lengths from scales, that the younger smolts have grown faster than the older ones. Figure 4, p. 31 from my early work on the Salmon of the Welsh Dee (Jones, 1939) is based on the estimation of length, using the adult scale markings (see Chapter 3, p. 43, for a discussion of the limitations of this method). It shows that the yearling migrants at the end of the first year of their life were 2·9 inches in length and were thus longer than any of the older migrants at this age (two-year-olds average 2·2 inches, three-year-olds average 1·6 inches); similarly, the two-year-old smolts were of a greater length at the end of each year of life than those which had remained three or more years in the rivers. It may be concluded that as a general rule parr, even in the same river, grow at different rates, and that the faster they grow, the sooner they turn into smolts. (Plate 5a-d, p. 52, shows scales of yearling, two-year-old, and three-year-old smolts).

There is little doubt that the old couplet

The first spate of May
Takes the smolts away.

tells one when the smolts generally leave the river, but there is more to it than that. When, before they migrate seawards in May, June, or even July, the parr are changing into smolts, the most obvious external indication is the way in which the parr-marks and spots become obliterated by a deposition of silvery guanine in the epidermis. The guanine may be present as a thin layer in late March, and is well established by the middle of April. It is an excretory product whose visible presence is a sign of the considerable internal physiological changes taking place to enable the fish to pass from a fresh-water to a marine environment.

The production of the guanine coat has interested many workers. Landgrebe (1941) produced a marked silveriness in six Salmon parr by injecting them with an extract of ox thyroid gland; two months after the injection the parr-markings were completely obliterated. Another batch of fish injected with an

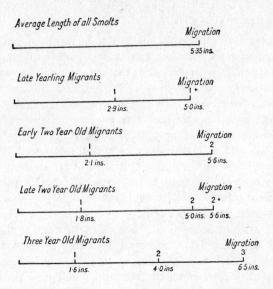

FIG. 4. Calculated yearly lengths and lengths at migration of yearling, two-year-old, and three-year-old Welsh Dee Salmon smolts

extract of the anterior lobe of the pituitary gland of an ox also became silvery; he suggests that the silveriness which followed injection was probably due to the stimulation of the animals' own thyroid gland, and was independent of the development of the gonads. This latter conclusion has confirmed our own findings (Jones and Orton, 1940). We examined a large number of smolts and found that most of the males had already matured sexually and had then discharged or absorbed their sperms before turning into smolts; others, however, were still immature, and so were all the females. It is therefore quite apparent that sexual maturity has nothing directly to do with the development of the seaward migratory urge or to the production of the silvery coat of guanine.

Hoar *et al.* (1951) assert that in their experiments pituitary and thyroid solutions sometimes failed to produce a pronounced development of the guanine coat, and add that "these findings substantiate the idea that the thyroid hormone in some way promotes the deposition of guanine in the skin of salmonids but does not specifically control the reaction. Thyroid compounds, in high concentration, produce silvering, but normal guanine deposition occurs without pronounced thyroid activity and is not interfered with by the antithyroid drug, thiourea." After a discussion of the experimental work of Fontaine and other investigators (1948), Hoar concludes that the development of the smolt coat requires something in addition to the thyroid hormone. Clearly we still have much to learn about the physiological development of the smolts and the control of their seaward migration (see also Hoar 1952).

There are not many fishes that can withstand a change from fresh into salt water or vice versa; probably the best known are the "fresh-water" eels, the fish of the salmon family and the sticklebacks. Fishes which can contend with such drastic changes in external medium are said to be *euryhaline* (Gr: euros, broad: hals, salt), whereas those that cannot survive a great change in salinity are called *stenohaline* (Gr. stenos, narrow).

Changes in weight take place if the euryhaline eel is transferred from fresh to sea-water or vice versa (Keys and Wilmer, 1932), (Keys, 1932-33). When the fish is adapted to one or other environment, its osmotic regulation in that medium is probably the same as that of those stenohaline fish which live permanently in it. But if an eel which is adapted to fresh water is transferred into sea-water, it undergoes a loss of weight resulting from loss of water; after about ten days this loss stops, an equilibrium is reached and the eel starts to gain weight. Similarly, when an eel which is adapted to sea-water is transferred into fresh water, it gains weight rapidly due to absorption of water, until eventually a steady state is reached. This absorption of water on moving from sea to fresh water "thins the blood": for example the blood of the Pacific King-salmon is diluted about 12 per cent by the time it reaches its spawning grounds, and similar figures have been obtained for the Atlantic Salmon.

When in sea-water the eel needs some means of controlling the

Plate 3a. A newly hatched salmon alevin, and an egg almost ready to hatch. (*Francis Ward*)

b. A salmon bed opened to show some of the eggs ; in this case eight inches of gravel had been removed to expose these eggs, very many more are not yet visible. (*J. W. Jones*)

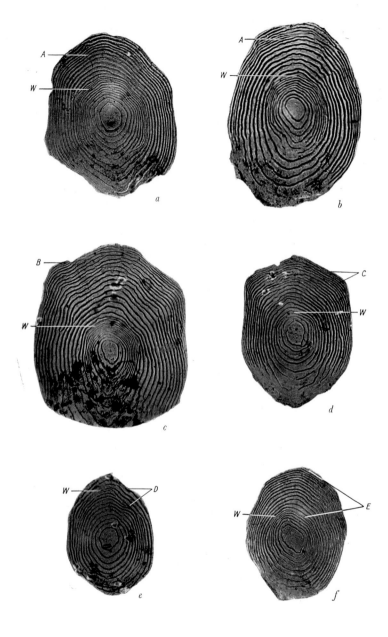

salt-content of the body, otherwise the salts might reach a lethal concentration. Keys and Wilmer found that the gills of the eels contain some special "chloride-excreting cells", which apparently secrete chloride ions into the surrounding water. Copeland found similar cells in *Fundulus;* if this fish had been acclimatized to sea-water, the cells had in them vesicles which were thought to be excretory and to pass out salt; in fresh water these cells had no vesicles and presumably were inactive. I suggested in 1947 that Salmon smolts might possess a similar mechanism in order to withstand the change from fresh to sea-water; recently such cells have been found in the gills of Salmon smolts by workers in Liverpool (I. Chester Jones, unpublished). Later work, however, shows that excretion of sodium ions can take place *via* the gills in the absence of such cells (Holmes, unpublished). It may well be that Bevelander's (1935 and 1936) opinion that these cells are only or mainly concerned in mucus-production is the correct interpretation of their function. Many physiological aspects of the seaward migration of young Salmon are clearly not yet fully understood.

Smolts move down to the sea in shoals sometimes numbering thousands. On their journey they feed voraciously: in the Dee

---

Plate 4 (opposite)

a. and b. Two two-year-old salmon parr scales taken in October showing summer check rings at *A*.   (*Irvine and Fleming*)

c. and d. Two two-year-old salmon parr scales with winter growth rings at their edges.
  c is from a fish killed in October and shows two winter rings at *B*.
  d is from a fish killed in February and shows a fully developed winter band of narrowly spaced rings at *C*.   (*Irvine and Fleming*)

e. and f. *e* is a scale from a fish in its second summer of life, killed in May, and showing widely spaced summer rings at *D*. 1st winter band labelled *W*.
  f. this fish was also in its second summer of life, but was killed in September and two types of summer rings can be seen in the second summer band of rings, the wide ones following immediately on the first winter band (*W*) and the narrow summer rings towards the edge of the scale.   (*Irvine and Fleming*)

at Chester, for instance, they can be seen rising all over the river. Anglers regard them as a nuisance at this time of year, as they will take almost any bait put in the river and it is illegal to keep them. It is unfortunate that so many are caught in this manner. They cannot stand much handling; their scales rub off very easily; and, though I have no proof, I think that at this crucial stage in their life-history it is harmful for them to lose their scales. In fast-moving waters the smolts drop downstream tail first, but in a smooth current of, say, one mile per hour, they are said to swim actively downstream. I have spent many hours watching and catching smolts at what used to be the Hydroelectric Station at Chester. Here the smolts moved down the race to the turbines tail first, usually on the surface of the water, only darting into deeper water when alarmed. On reaching the grid, they would move along it with their tails appearing to touch it; if one slipped through several others in the shoal would follow tail first. From my observations at Chester there was no indication that the smolts had any preference for moving downstream at any particular time of the day or night, and shoals arrived at the grid at all hours.

Calderwood (1945) is of the opinion that smolts can pass unharmed through turbines; he carried out experiments with smolts at the Tongland station of the Galloway Water Power Company. There were some casualties when the turbines were running on light load, but on full load, when the vanes of the turbines opened automatically to their full extent, only one was killed and nine stunned out of the thousands that passed through. He also carried out tests with more modern turbines, and came to the conclusion that the pressures generated in the turbines (72 lb. to the square inch) did not damage the air-bladder of the trout used in his experiments. At a pressure of 150 lb. the trout turned over on their sides, but when the pressure was reduced they regained their upright position and swam about normally. It should, however, be mentioned that opinion is far from unanimous about the harmlessness of turbines.*

* See also, 1957 'The passage of Smolts and Kelts through Fish passes' H.M. Stationery Office, London.

The behaviour of the young of the Chum, Pink and Coho salmon on their migration to the sea has been studied by Hoar (1951, 1954, 1956). He found that "In fresh water they form schools or mills, are constantly active, both day and night, show positive rheotaxis and move into fast water. This activity takes them into the swiftest currents. At night loss of visual and contact stimuli reduces the intensity of the rheotactic response and results in downstream movement. An active swimming downstream occurs only with unusually high temperatures. Coho salmon fry occupy and defend territory, maintain definite positions in relation to particular objects in their environment, show a marked tendency to move into fast water and are quiet at night. They are thus displaced downstream to a much lesser degree. Coho smolts, in contrast to the fry, demonstrate a lowered threshold for stimulation both day and night, a tendency to aggregate and a lessening in territory behaviour. During the day smolts group in deeper water or under cover. At night they rise to the surface and manifest increased activity which, in swift water, will result in displacement seawards. Profound changes modify these reactions. Sudden elevation of water levels hastens them downstream." Chum and Pink salmon do not become smolty, and according to Hoar show no evidence of a change in their internal physiology before moving to the sea. The Coho, however, show a transformation into smolts and with this change in internal physiology there also occurs a change in behaviour patterns. Thus Coho and Pink salmon fry are continually on the move, both day and night, and this activity brings them into regions of the river where there are swift currents; in the experiments these fish appeared to prefer to lie in the fastest currents. Rheotaxis is dependent in part on visual stimuli, also mechanical stimuli developed by the turbulence of water flowing round solid objects, and also labyrinthine reflexes brought about by rotating currents (Gray, 1937; Hoagland, 1935). At night the visual stimulus is reduced or lost, and the schools break up; also, as the light intensity is reduced, the fish rise to the surface, and thereby lose or have reduced contact stimuli. As these fish are very active at night Hoar concludes from this and the above observation that their downstream movement is inevitable. In addition, at high temperatures and at rapidly rising temperatures the Chum salmon develop increased activity which results in the fish swimming downstream more rapidly than the currents (negative rheotaxis). Hoar also points out that as Chum and Pink salmon "are poorly adjusted [osmotically?] to fresh water, they experience a high mortality when retained in this environment." (Hoar and Bell, 1950).

On the other hand, Coho fry maintain their positions at night; they settle on the bottom. During the day they relate themselves to objects in the stream, and thus tend to have a prolonged residence in one area. The Coho smolts, like the Atlantic Salmon smolts, put on a silvery migration coat, and at the same time show the changes in behaviour described above.

In 1953, MacKinnon and Hoar made additional observations on the behaviour of Chum salmon fry and concluded that they did not move into the "swiftest currents" though they did prefer faster currents than other Pacific salmon. Smolts of the Sockeye salmon are more active than Coho smolts, and their movement seaward, Hoar suggests, is due to an increased activity both day and night, this being associated with a strong response to current. During the day they swim vigorously against the current and maintain their position in the stream, but at night, when the rheotactic response is reduced, they swim less vigorously and are carried downstream.

Rheotaxis is a dangerous term to use because in its application to fish it has two different meanings, superficially similar, but fundamentally distinct. In the first of these meanings it describes the normal "station-keeping" behaviour of a fish "resting" at a fixed point in a stream. This type of response is predominantly of visual origin: the fish swims against the current just fast enough to keep visible objects on the bank and bottom stationary in its visual field, as can very easily be demonstrated under laboratory conditions. In its second meaning rheotaxis describes the behaviour of a fish in seeking out a current and (usually) setting itself with its head upstream. This type of behaviour is less easy to observe and is not so well understood. But if there is a place in a stream where the current is a maximum it is a necessary hydro-dynamic consequence that at every other place there will be a velocity gradient. The lateral-line sense-organs of fishes appear to have been evolved (among other purposes) for the detection of velocity gradients, and it has been shown that they are sensitive to very small gradients indeed. If, therefore, a fish were to go on swimming until its left and right lateral-line organs were stimulated to an equal and minimal degree it would eventually find itself floating in the fastest part of the current with its head either downstream or up (but not across). This is probably a much over-simplified explanation of what actually happens; but that the lateral-line organs are involved is extremely likely.

I have said that the "station-keeping" rheotaxis is predomin-antly of visual origin: certainly it often appears to be suppressed in the dark. In nature fish often move down at night until their ventral fins actually touch the bottom and touch takes over from vision. There is, however, some evidence that blind cave-fish and stream-fish which have been blinded can, in certain circumstances, keep station without having any solid contact, and it is surmised that here the lateral-line organs play a part. It is easy to see how this could happen in a stream in which the bottom is not perfectly regular, for every projecting stone will alter the entire con-figuration of current velocities in its neighbourhood, and so may act as a landmark to a fish which is neither touching it nor able to see it.

Little consideration is needed to see that both the rheotactic mechanisms described can be invoked to explain, at least in part, the formation and behaviour of shoals or schools of fish; and the frequent association of shoaling with up or downstream migration is unlikely to be only coincidental.

The existence of two distinct rheotactic types of behaviour, either of which may dominate or reinforce the other, and one of which is frequently suppressed in the dark, makes it easier to understand Hoar's rather puzzling observations and to recon-cile their apparent conflict with observations on Atlantic Salmon.

Unlike the Pacific salmon smolts, those of the Atlantic Salmon which arrive at Chester, not far from tidal water, in May and

June, move downstream throughout the day and night; at this stage in their journey their smolt coat is very well developed. Some of these smolts were transferred to the Liverpool University Marine Biological Station at Port Erin, Isle of Man, where an unlimited amount of pure sea-water was available. After being given time to get over any ill effects resulting from the journey, batches of the smolts were subjected to changes from fresh to salt water effected at different rates. In each experiment where smolts were transferred directly into sea-water, the fish became sluggish in an hour or so, and after two hours the fish lay on their sides at the bottom of the tank, they had little interest in life, they could be prodded and lifted out of the water by their dorsal fin without offering any resistance to such treatment. In one such experiment the fish died within a day; in another, the fish were sluggish after two hours, but at this stage the sea-water was turned off and fresh water run into the tank. Within five and a half hours, the fish were again very lively and apparently normal. There is little doubt that these fish could not withstand a sudden transfer from fresh to salt water. Other smolts were placed in separate tanks of fresh water into which sea-water was run at different rates, so that the change from fresh to salt water was accomplished in different lengths of time. If the change of medium took ten hours or longer, the smolts survived. (Jones, 1947). These experiments were repeated at the Hydroelectric Station at Chester, the smolts being caught here and subjected to the various transfers almost immediately after capture. Clean sea-water was obtained for these experiments at Hoylake on the Irish Sea. Despite the high temperature of about 20°C in daytime, similar results were obtained (Jones, unpublished), and as in the Manx experiment, there were no deaths or signs of sluggishness in any of the fish in any of the control experiments.

It was observed in the "direct transfer" experiments from fresh to sea-water, that as the fish became more and more sluggish they showed considerable colour-changes, and at times their eyes appeared opaque, and apparently non-functional, as no response was given to movement of objects in the water in close proximity to the head. Some observations of other investigators are in

38

agreement with the Chester and Manx results. As long ago as 1871, Bert found that young Salmon eventually died when placed directly in sea-water; an alevin died in one and a half hours, and a 12 cm. parr in six. Hayes and M'Conigle also found that fry and parr died in sea-water. But Day (1887) believes that silvery smolts could, after they had been silvery for some time, be put directly into sea-water without injury. Day also gives an interesting account of an experiment carried out in 1879-80 at Brighton Aquarium by a Mr. Francis Francis. About twenty small parr were placed in a fresh-water tank; eight months later in the following May, some assumed the smolt livery, but four remained "golden parrs". Salt water was gradually introduced; this did not prove fatal to the parr and the smolts "became rampant with pleasure". When the water was fully sea-water, the parr started becoming silvery, "they ate five times as much as previously, were in rapid and incessant motion all day, and their growth became perfectly astonishing". Others have found that Salmon smolts would survive a sudden transfer from fresh to salt water (Roberts and Jee, 1922) and attempts to acclimatize parr to sea water by gradually increasing the proportion of sea-water in their tank or by gradually increasing the duration of exposure to a mixture of sea and fresh water have sometimes been partially successful (Chaisson, 1933).

In order to find out whether the ability of Salmon parr to withstand sea-water develops gradually during the river life of the young fish, or whether it is acquired abruptly as the transformation into smolts takes place, Huntsman and Hoar (1939) subjected parr of various sizes to sea-water of different salinities: they found that all sizes of fish died in the higher salinities ($28^0/_{00}$) but survived in the lower ones ($10^0/_{00}$). The higher the salinity, the shorter the survival time: also, the larger the fish, the longer it survived in the high salinity. They conclude "that Salmon parr, as they increase in size, become more resistant to sea-water only to the degree to which the exposed surfaces through which the sea-water must act, become less in proportion to the mass of the body, in particular the blood. Evidence fails to show any increase in the resistance of the tissues to sea-water.

"It follows that the Salmon develops rather abruptly, when transforming from the parr to the smolt stage, the ability to live in sea-water."

Huntsman and Hoar state that "in nature smolts descend to the sea, and doubtless not infrequently pass quite abruptly from river to sea-water." As observed in June of 1936 at the mouth of the Margaree River, Cape Breton Island, they are quite inactive for a time after entering the sea-water abruptly, and may be seen scattered near the bottom where there is little movement of the sea-water. Although able to withstand sudden change, they seem to be unfavourably affected by it for a time. Mr. Menzies tells me that there are many rivers in Scotland where the transition from fresh to sea-water must be abrupt; but abruptness is a matter of degree and it seems certain that, owing to tidal stirring, there will always be a boundary layer of intermediate concentration in which smolts could remain until they got used to it. In larger rivers, where the volume of fresh water is great, it is conceivable that the smolts can easily spend as long as ten hours in brackish fresh water or dilute sea-water, and thus have plenty of time to become acclimatized to the change of medium. Thus they will avoid the risk of being immobilized and so falling an easy prey to cormorants and gulls, and the various predators that await their entry into the sea.

It is believed by many that seals are enemies of smolts as well as of the returning adults, though there is no evidence of this. MacIntyre (1947) points out that seals have increased in number immensely within his lifetime; he gives several instances of seals being seen chasing and eating Salmon, and also says, without supporting evidence, that seals prefer Salmon to any other fish. But before any massacre of seals can be justified, an examination ought to be made of stomachs of representative samples of seals over a period of at least twelve months. On the other hand, cormorants have definitely been incriminated in a few localities by examination of their stomachs and one caught on the River Forss had recently eaten forty smolts. Even this does not justify a wholesale massacre of cormorants without a much more thorough enquiry.

It has often been suggested that there is a second migration of smolts in August and September. Such runs were reported in the Severn at Shrewsbury (Day, 1887, p. 91), Teme, Avon, Wye, Erne and Trent. I have not seen any of these late smolts, even though fairly recently (1940) I was informed whilst I was working on the Hampshire and Dorset rivers that late smolts were thought to run down the Piddle (Dorset). Unfortunately none of these fish were caught during my stay there.

Let us return now to a further consideration of the urge which compels the smolts to their downstream journey to the sea. The old rhyme quoted above (p. 30) correctly expresses the truth that migration occurs when an appropriate stimulus (a spate) is applied to fish which are in the appropriate physiological condition (smolts). According to Bull (1930), a spate (in the Tyne) as small as is caused by $\frac{1}{10}$th inch of rain falling locally in 24 hours, may be effective; but whether such a shower is enough or a considerable flood is needed almost certainly depends on how long the smolts have had to wait for it. White (1939) found that the descent of smolts was determined by a rise in temperature and low light intensity, not by rainfall or rise in water-level. It has been shown in many more carefully studied examples of animal behaviour, that the longer an "urge" is bottled up, the smaller is the stimulus necessary to release it.

We are therefore back to the fundamental question of what makes a smolt. We have seen already that the conversion of a parr into a smolt has nothing to do with sexual development and is not directly concerned with size. On the other hand, there is strong evidence that it is dependent on *rate* of growth. The parr which (in nature) turn earliest into smolts are those which have been growing fastest. In experimental conditions parr can sometimes be turned into smolts by treatment with the secretions of endocrine glands (thyroid and anterior pituitary) which are known in some other animals to be concerned with the regulation of rate of growth. According to Mr. Francis Francis, acclimatization to sea-water may also be effective, but as he also commented on the astonishing growth-rate of his parr, he may well have attributed the conversion to the wrong cause.

The reason why some parr should grow faster than others cannot yet be specifically stated, but it is probably a combination of genetic and environmental factors (as, indeed, differential growth rates is known to be due to in man and other animals). The greater age of smolts in northern rivers indicates an environmental factor, though whether this is shortage of light or shortage of food or a lower mean temperature is a matter of speculation. The fact that, in the same river and with access to the same food, parr in this country may take one, two or three years to attain smolt-hood suggests that the growth-rate is also influenced by genetic factors. Such evidence as is available indicates that the inherited factor leading to early conversion from parr to smolt is not a preference for a particular and profitable kind of food, but a heightened intensity of all food-seeking activities which may well reflect an inherited enhancement of endocrine function. And there we must leave the problem, for the complexities of endocrine function in fish constitute a wilderness whose exploration is only just beginning.

CHAPTER 3

SCALES AND SCALE-READING

AS has been indicated in the foregoing chapters, much of our knowledge about Salmon has been obtained by studying their scales. By this means it is possible to tell not only how old a full-grown fish is, but which years it has spent in the river and which in the sea. Its size in each past year of its life can be assessed, and its rate of growth can be compared with that of other fish. When it spawned previously, how long it stayed in the sea between spawnings, how old and how big it was when it left the river as a smolt—all these can be assessed, because the scale is a growing part of the body and the spacing of the rings on it is an indication of the rate of its owner's growth in the period when the rings were being formed.

The scales first appear as papillae on the anterior and middle of the body along the lateral-line, when the fish are about an inch in length; those at the posterior end are invisible at this stage. From these primary papillae dorsal and ventral extensions grow out obliquely forward. At intervals along each of these outgrowths further papillae arise. (The scale count used as a specific character for Salmon and trout (see Appendix I, p. 154) actually runs downwards and obliquely forwards from the adipose fin to the lateral-line, and thus is not along an axis of scale development).

A fully developed scale consists of a hard outer and a fibrous inner layer. The outer layer is a kind of bone called hyalodentine related to the dentine of our teeth, as is to be expected since scales and teeth have a common evolutionary background, both consisting of an organic framework and certain inorganic salts, principally calcium phosphate and calcium carbonate. Its genesis is a complicated story and readers are referred to papers by Setna (1934) and Neave (1936) for details. The result is a flat platelet, the outer surface of which is ridged, and which (as shown in Fig. 5, p. 44) lies abliquely in a pocket in the dermis. The posterior portion of the scale projects above the surface of the dermis and overlaps the scales behind. The scales are covered by the epidermis, which consists of several layers of cells. The pigment of the young fish is not carried in or on the scales, but deeper in the skin.

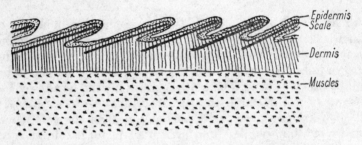

FIG. 5. Diagram to show position of scales in the skin of Salmon

In the course of growth, ridges are formed successively around a small unringed centre or nucleus on the outer surface of the scale. It has been suggested that the cells (scleroblasts) build the scale by secreting its substance and at its growing edge make a thick portion which is hollowed out behind by the action of more deeply seated cells (scleroclasts); these break down and absorb part of the hyalodentine to leave a ridge. Although neither the method of formation of the ridges nor the reason for it is fully understood, their presence is of great importance in the study of fish growth. The ridges, or *rings*, as I prefer to call them, can be clearly seen when a scale is examined under a low-power microscope or a good hand-lens; they are present mainly on the embedded or inner portion of the scale (see diagram). The rings in a scale from an old fish can be seen to be grouped in alternate *bands*, of widely spaced (open) rings, and less widely spaced and less numerous (narrow) rings (Fig. 6, p. 45). It has long been accepted that the bands of wide rings represent periods in the life of the fish when growth was rapid, and that the bands of narrow rings represent periods of less rapid growth. These periods have been loosely termed "summer" growth and "winter" growth respectively, though the correspondence with these seasons is only rough. Dahl (1907) found (in Norway) that narrow "winter" rings were being formed in January, February and March and that "summer" rings were being formed throughout the other nine months of the year.

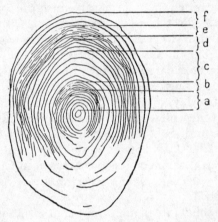

FIG. 6. An ideal two-year-old Salmon smolt scale (diagrammatic). *a*. first summer rings, *b*. first winter rings, *c*. second summer wide rings, *d*. second summer narrow rings, *e*. second winter rings, *f*. third summer (plus) growth rings

There has been some controversy about whether these rules are equally applicable in the first two years of river life (Arwidsson, 1910, and others). Their validity has however now been established by Went and Frost (1942) for brown trout and by myself (Jones, 1949) for Salmon parr, mainly from the Dee and Wnion, and also from eighteen other British Salmon rivers. It is therefore certain that "winter bands" on parr and smolt scales represent periods of slow growth which correspond approximately to the October to March season, though as might be expected there is some variation from year to year in any one river, and also a tendency for the formation of the "summer band" to begin earlier in the more southerly rivers. (Plates 4 a-f and 5 a-d p. 33 and 52 show the different rings found on parr and smolt scales).

In counting the rings on the scales of two-year-old parr and smolts, it was noticed that the rings formed in the second "summer" could generally be divided into two groups, (a) widely-spaced rings with almost uniform spacing which were laid down immediately after the first winter band of narrow rings, and (b) less widely-spaced rings in which the spacing between the rings usually decreased gradually and progressively until they merged almost imperceptibly into the second winter band. (Plate 4f, p. 33). Counts of these two types of summer rings were made on a large number of scales: it was found that the wide summer rings were well established on the scales of Welsh Dee parr in May, and that the narrow summer rings started to appear in June, and were fully established in July and continued to be formed until September/October (4e and f). As a result of this observation I am convinced that the "winter band" reported by Carr (1913) as having been completed in October was formed of narrowly spaced summer rings, and was not, in fact, a true winter band.*

The seasonal rate of appearance of the various types of growth rings on the scales of young Salmon is shown in Fig. 7, p. 47, and Plates 4a-f and 5a-d, p. 33 and 52. It is seen that the formation of rings is very slow between November and March: this is to be expected as only three or four rings, and sometimes only two, are laid down during the winter. The second-summer rings are laid down rapidly and evenly from April to July, then progressively more slowly and with narrower spacing until they grade almost imperceptibly into the winter band in November. Allen's claim that there was no detectable growth in winter of the parr in the Eden and Thurso is probably incorrect, as I have found a small but measurable growth in length (average 5 per cent) for parr in their second winter (see Figs. 3, p. 27, and 7, p. 47) in the Welsh Dee; but there is no reason to doubt his conclusion that

---

* Winter bands of rings may be completely formed on the scales of Llyn Tegid (Bala) trout by the end of October (Ball and Jones in M.S.).

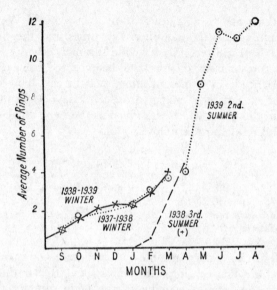

Fig. 7. Monthly increments in number of the various types of growth rings on the scales of Welsh Dee parr and smolts 1937–1939

.... = 2nd winter rings formed during 1937–38
x—x = 2nd winter rings formed during 1938–39
——— = 3rd summer rings (+) formed during 1938
.... = 2nd summer rings formed during 1939

summer growth is divisible into an early phase of rapid growth (April to July), and a later phase of gradually diminishing growth (August to October). His summer feeding periods therefore correspond reasonably with my periods of wide- and narrow-rings in the summer band on the scale (Plate 4f).

It is sometimes difficult to decide the extent of a seasonal band of rings, particularly when the late summer rings shade gradually into the winter band (Plate 4c and d). Generally, however, the winter rings are more broken than the late summer rings and are also slightly closer. The spacing of the three types of rings formed during the second year of life was investigated by measurements on the scales of a sample of fifty two-year-old Welsh Dee smolts. Each scale was magnified 150 times and the distances between each of the second-year-wide summer, narrow summer and winter rings measured. As was to be expected, some difficulty was experienced in differentiating accurately between the extremes of each type of ring. In order to have some means of comparison, the mean width was given as the percentage of scale length. The results are as follows:

Type of Ring	Number of ring spacings measured	Mean width of ring spacing × 100 length of scale
Wide Summer Rings	342	4·24
Narrow Summer Rings	174	2·82
Winter Rings	149	1·80

These figures are, of course, only approximate—great accuracy is not possible when dealing with scales; nevertheless they show clearly that the average spacing of the wide summer rings in relation to scale length was greater by about 50 per cent than that of the narrow summer rings, which in turn, are rather more than 50 per cent more widely spaced than the "winter" rings. These figures also give a fair indication of the proportional seasonal increase in total length, the ratio being probably 9:6:4 for spring and early summer growth, late summer growth and winter growth respectively.

There is usually no great difficulty in applying the rules so far established, but unfortunately there are further complications. One of these is the appearance (on the scales of perhaps 5 per cent in Britain of any large sample of young Salmon or trout) of the "summer-check" band of rings (Plate 4a and b). These are narrowly spaced rings indicating slower growth, and are often formed at the edge of the scale in the middle of the summer season which ought to be a period of active feeding. Such a band could easily be taken to be a winter band by an ignorant or inexperienced scale-reader, but fortunately it can usually, with practice, be distinguished. The discrimination of such a check-band from a winter band depends on the type of ring preceding it: in a normal winter band the transition from narrow summer rings to winter rings is usually so gradual that it is difficult to tell which is the last summer ring and which the first winter ring, whereas between the early summer rings and the first "check" ring the change-over is usually abrupt. Also, though possibly only to experienced scale-readers, the position of the summer check in relation to the previous band of winter rings often indicates that the check rings are not true winter rings: for instance, if a band of narrow rings on the scale is separated from the previous winter band by only three or four summer rings, and the normal complement of sum-mer rings between two winter bands is, say, fifteen rings, then suspicion of a summer check is confirmed (Jones 1949).

These summer check-bands probably indicate that the fish has suddenly stopped feeding and grown more slowly. Bhatia (1931) produced check-bands in the scales of trout by starvation. But the reason for the check in growth in natural conditions is not understood. Swift (1955) has shown that changes in the activity of the thyroid gland may occur in brown trout at this time, and brown trout may also exhibit summer-checks.

That the problem of checks is not a simple one is apparent from the reports of van Someren (1952) on the scales of trout introduced into streams in the uplands of Kenya. This is too near the equator for marked seasonal differences, and in fact the scale rings show no distinction of summer and winter bands. Check-bands however do still occur and may do so at any time in the year, though preponderantly in July and August.

In New Zealand, Allen (1951) found some difficulty in interpreting the scales of trout from the Horokiwi streams, because of the confusing growth-rates obtained from calculating lengths from scales of trout from this stream and comparing them with similar figures for trout from the Hutt stream. He suggested that these differences in growth-rates resulted from either the abnormally high growth-rate of the Horokiwi trout compared with the Hutt trout, or else from a fault in the scale-reading technique. He favoured the latter suggestion: I think that the differences are more probably the result of wrong application of the scale-reading technique. Allen writes of the appearance in the first summer of a "point at which a *fairly abrupt* increase in width occurs giving an appearance similar to the commencement of 'summer' growth after a 'winter' band" (my italics). He is probably here describing growth after a "summer-check", and it is likely that previously this type of check has been mis-interpreted to represent a "winter" band, with the result that anomalous growth-rates have been estimated from examination of the scales.

So far we have dealt only with the scales of the young fish in the river. Rings are formed on the scales of Salmon and sea-trout in the sea in a similar way, and these rings also are grouped into wide and narrowly spaced rings, i.e. summer and winter bands. Once the Salmon starts feeding in the sea it grows rapidly; and this increased growth-rate is very obviously reflected in the size and spacing of the rings on its scales. Sea-rings are robust and much more widely spaced than any of the rings laid down in the river (see Plates 5e and 6, p. 52 and 53). The change-over from river-ring to sea-ring formation is not always sudden or clear-cut, probably because some smolts hang around in the estuary for a considerable time. A few rings of intermediate breadth may often be seen on the scale in between the true river- and the true sea-rings these are often called estuarine growth-rings.

Even when adult, Salmon are not infrequently confused with sea-trout and brown trout, for the ranges of variation in colour and shape of each type overlap, and each may be caught in unexpected places. In such cases the scale-reader is often the ultimate court of appeal. For example, a 22 lb. fish of the Salmon family, caught in 1954 in the River Nadder (Wilts.), was at first believed to be an abnormally large brown trout. An examination of a scale, however, showed fine river-growth rings in the centre surrounded by robust sea-rings (Plate 5e). The fish had therefore migrated to the sea and returned again to fresh water, and must be either a Salmon or a sea-trout. But a sea-trout of such a size would have spawned several times and the absence of spawning marks (see below) was a clear indication that the fish was in fact a Salmon. So a single scale can, if necessary, be used to determine whether fish are Salmon, sea-trout, or brown trout, though it is always desirable for the scale-reader to be able to examine the whole fish when this is practicable, and to be aware of any other circumstantial evidence. I experienced the danger of relying entirely on scales when those of a 5 lb. trout were sent to me from the Isle of Man. I examined them and saw what I thought to be undoubtedly a parr centre of fine rings followed by a series of robust "sea" rings. Having committed myself to the opinion that this fish was a sea-trout which had spent two years in the river as a parr before migrating to the sea, I was told that the fish had been caught in water which had no inlet or outlet! It eventually transpired that the 5 lb. trout was one of a number which had been transferred at the age of two from very poor water to a very rich pond, and the greatly accelerated growth which took place in consequence was reflected in their scales, giving the appearance of sea-growth rings

In assessing sea-age care must be taken to differentiate between "summer-checks" in feeding and the true winter band. But even when all precautions have been taken and long experience is brought to bear, some scales cannot be read: and the longer they are examined the less sense they make. The Salmon from which such scales come are very few in number and it is better to admit defeat and classify them as unreadable than to guess at random. Other scales may be quite unreadable because the central rings (i.e., the river-rings and often many of the sea-rings) are missing—having been replaced by clear scale matrix. These are the so-called "accident" or replacement scales (see Plate 5f, p. 52), which are formed in the scale pockets in replacement of any of the original scales which have been rubbed off. The centres are blank because it is not possible for the scale-producing mechanism to "go back in time" and repeat the past history of the fish.

It is most important that scales used for age-calculation should have the original nucleus. In rivers where parr growth is poor three or four rings only are laid down in the summer and only one or two in the first winter, thus a slightly enlarged accident centre may encompass one year of life. Many scale-reading errors are due to misinterpretation of the first year: many so-called 1+ smolts are in fact 2+ smolts. It is only with much practice and patience that an original scale-nucleus can be recognised.

Scales of Salmon which have spawned and returned to the sea, and are coming back for a second (or more rarely third) spawning, bear on them a *spawning mark*. The scale shown in Plate 7, p. 60, bears one such mark. It is the result of the erosion or absorption of the scale margin, and in some cases of the surface also. Erosion is the result of the activity of the cells near the margin of the scale, which (when it is growing normally) lay down the scale material: in other words, the normal functioning of these cells is reversed (Crichton, 1935, Blair, 1942). Crichton's suggestion that scale erosion is a consequence of calcium deficiency in the fasting period is probably correct, but his association of the calcium deficiency with the remodelling of the skull-bones of the male is more doubtful. The spawning marks are often as obvious in the scales of the female as in those of the male.

Erosion of the scale starts at the scale shoulders, that is at the ends of the junction between the ring-bearing portion and the part which bears no rings—and which is, of course, the part which is not overlapped by the scales in front. It gradually spreads from these points around the edges of the inner ring-bearing portion; and the projecting portion of the scale is very much less affected. In extreme cases, especially on the scales of large early-running male Salmon, erosion may be so great that much of the scale disappears; the remainder has a triangular outline.*

* For estimating the amount of erosion that has taken place, the posterior part of the scale is divided into zones as shown in Fig. 8, p. 53; an erosion of 6 will extend to the apex of the scale, etc.

Plate 5 (opposite)
a. and *b.* Two smolt scales from two-year-old fish showing third summer rings at their edges. (*Irvine and Fleming*)
c. and *d.* Scales from a yearling, and a three-year-old smolt. Both fish killed in May. (*Irvine and Fleming*)
e. The controversial Nadder "trout" scale. (*Irvine*)
f. An accident or replacement scale. (*Irvine*)

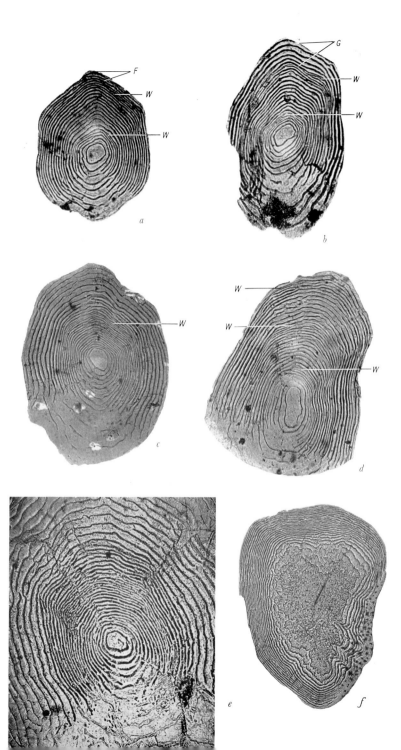

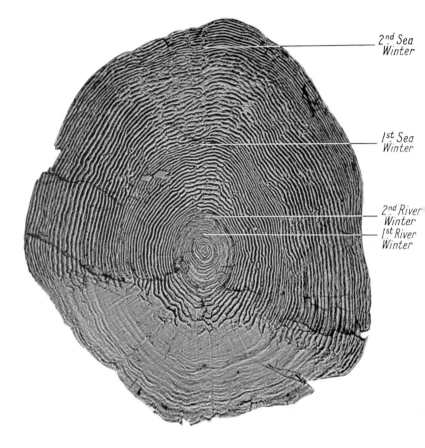

2nd Sea
Winter

1st Sea
Winter

2nd River
Winter
1st River
Winter

Plate 6. Scale of small summer fish. Two years in the river, two + years in the sea. (*Irvine*)

Scale-erosion is clearly the result of some physiological change which is taking place in the fish, and is a consequence of the production of a proportionately very large mass of eggs or milt at a time when the fish is taking no nourishment. The spawning mark is not evidence that the fish has actually spawned. The few female Salmon (called baggots or rawners), which for lack of opportunity or other reasons do not spawn and which ultimately re-absorb their unshed genital products, probably show a spawning mark (though this does not appear to have been definitely established). On the other hand, male Salmon parr may spawn without in fact showing a spawning mark (Jones 1949).

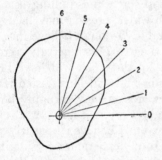

Fig 8. A scale sub-divided to show the areas of erosion

Although erosion is the consequence of simultaneous fasting and active development of the gonads, other factors must also be involved. The extent of the erosion is also dependent on the time the Salmon spend in the river. It is much greater in spring-fish than in autumn-fish: in late-autumn-fish it may be so slight that some authorities have doubted whether it is always recognizable. Yet in these late-runners maturation of the gonads is far advanced when the fish enter the river; and such evidence as is available indicates that they have already been fasting in the sea. It appears, therefore, that living in fresh water imposes a burden on the Salmon's economy in addition to the effects of fasting and gonad maturation.

Absorption continues until the fish returns to the sea and begins to feed again. As the fish recuperate, new material is added to the edge of the scale, and this, at its junction with the serrated or ragged portion, forms the scar—the "spawning mark" (Plate 7, p. 60). This new scale material fills in the gaps in the scale-edge and generally "rounds it off"; the gaps produced by surface erosion are not usually filled in. As soon as the damaged portions have been to some extent replaced, normal scale growth proceeds and rings are once more produced. But, obviously, owing to the loss of scale material around the edge, scales with spawning marks are not suitable for estimations of the length of the fish at any age before spawning: often too, such scales cannot safely be used to assess age because a complete winter band and more may have been eroded away.

It has been suggested that, in some late-running fish which spend only a short time in fresh water, erosion may be so slight that no spawning mark is detectable. I do not believe this. Very late-runners may arrive in the river in December and return to the sea in February, but, even so, these fish will have been in fresh water for nearly two months and will have fasted for very much longer. In such instances erosion may certainly be comparatively slight and not readily recognisable in a cursory examination of the mended scale, but I believe it is nearly always detectable on careful scrutiny. In my experience erosion in such cases is only evident along the lateral-edges of the scale; fortunately, such doubtful scales are rare.

Many attempts have been made to calculate the length of a Salmon at the end of each year of life from the disposition of the rings on its scales at capture, so as to obtain some idea of its growth-rate. The simplest basis of calculation is the assumption that throughout a Salmon's life the increase in the length of its scale is proportional to the increase in length of the fish. The relevant formula may be written as follows:

$$L_n = \frac{S_n L}{S}$$

where L_n = length of the fish at the end of nth year of life; S_n = distance from the centre of the first ring to the outer edge of the nth winter band of rings; L = length of fish at capture;

S=distance from the centre of the first ring to the anterior edge of the scale.

A moment's thought discloses that there is a second concealed assumption underlying this expression, namely, that the fish and its scales begin to grow at the same instant. This is certainly not true: as has been stated above, the fry may be between 1 and 2 inches long before any scales are formed. Lee (1920) proposed to take account of this, and his modified formula is sometimes used:

$$L_n = C + \frac{S_n(L-C)}{S}$$

where C is the length of the fish at the time when scales on its shoulder begin their growth, and the other symbols have the same meaning as before.

There is obviously no way of arriving at a precise value for C in any given fish, but if it is given an arbitrary mean value of say $1\frac{1}{2}$ inches, a rather closer approximation to the truth may be obtained than is given by the uncorrected formula. If the uncorrected formula is used, say, to assess from the scale of a Salmon how big it was as a smolt, it certainly gives results which are improbably small (p. 31). Not all authorities, however, are convinced of the desirability of Lee's correction; and Tate Regan emphatically maintained that scales (once they were formed) grew fast until they "caught up with" the growth of the body. This appears to be so in *Leucichthys artedi* (van Oosten, 1929) in which the ratio of body-length to scale-length decreases rapidly with age and growth in the first year of life; that is, in early life (up to the age of three) the scales increase in length much faster relatively than the body.

Many other formulae and corrections have been proposed: Huntsman (1918), Jarvi (1920), Sherriff (1922), Creaser (1926), Monastyrsky (1926), van Oosten (1923, 1929 and 1941), but all of these involve assumptions which could not be proved to be justified except by very large, very long, and very expensive experiments. The difficulty of reading the small central part of a large scale itself introduces errors which vitiate any accurate computation of absolute lengths of young Salmon from old scales, and it is doubtful whether much is gained in the present state of our knowledge by departing from the initial assumption of proportionality throughout life.

It should be emphasized that in many, perhaps most, applications of scale-reading what is wanted is not the assessment of absolute length, but that of relative growth-rate. This does not depend to anything like the same extent on the precise formula used for the computation. The statement that Salmon A grew 10 per cent faster than Salmon B in their second year as parr may be correct within a small limit of error even if their absolute computed lengths are perhaps too small by 30 per cent or even more.

So much of our knowledge of Salmon depends on the right interpretation of scales, that it seemed desirable to put this rather technical chapter early in the book. From now on the reader should keep before his mind's eye both the power of scale-reading and its limitations, the necessity of using it and the danger of relying on it too much (see Chapter 5).

CHAPTER 4

THE SALMON IN THE SEA

ONCE the smolts leave our rivers, we see little or nothing of them: we do not know where they go to; there is no evidence to show that they stay near our coasts. It is almost certain that our east coast Salmon do not stay to feed in the North Sea, otherwise they would be caught in greater numbers by North Sea fishermen. On the other hand, Dahl and Sømme (1944) report that Salmon smolts are often caught in the Baltic Sea, and were able to show that six months after entering the sea the smolts had travelled as far as six hundred miles from the river of their birth. However, Huntsman (1938) maintains that in Canada some of the smolts of the Atlantic Salmon which migrate into the Bay of Fundy do not move very far from the mouths of the rivers in which they were born; he has caught Salmon there after six months or even a year in the sea. The first we usually see of our Salmon is when they enter our rivers again after at least a year and a half in the sea.

Netting experiments carried out in the Bay of Fundy show that many Salmon do not move more than fifty miles from their native river, and Huntsman believes that they are still within its "zone of influence". The movements of the fish in the Bay are quite unrelated to the tides. But not all rivers are large enough to have such a zone of influence in the sea as the River St. John; and Huntsman believes that Salmon from smaller rivers may move further out to sea. If he is right in his assumption that Salmon tend to stay in that part of the sea in which the effect of the fresh water is felt, except where the rivers are too small to have any such effect, then it would appear that all our British rivers fall into this second (small) category. Consequently our Salmon probably move far out into the sea, and this explains why so few are caught in the open sea around Britain.

For very many years attempts have been made to discover the movements of the Salmon in the sea by tagging the fish. These experiments are based on a long-accepted fact that Salmon come into our inshore waters at various points along our coasts and migrate for varying distances along the shore before eventually entering fresh water. A considerable amount of tagging has been done in Canada, Scotland, Scandinavia, Ireland and England. The fish are netted or trapped in various ways and numbered tags are generally placed in the flesh of the fish at the anterior end of the dorsal fin (Fig. 1, p. 4). Probably the most efficient tag used to date is that made by Einar Lea of Norway. This tag, the Lea Hydrostatic tag, is made of a tube of transparent celluloid about two inches long and about an eighth of an inch in diameter, sealed at either end, numbered, and enclosing a letter. Externally the tag is marked *"Cut ends. Letter inside. Reward"*, in English and often two other languages. The paper inside asks for information about place and date of capture, gear used, length and weight of fish, and a request for scales to be removed from the shoulder (the region below and slightly in front of the dorsal fin) of the fish and sent to a certain address.

A vast number of adult Atlantic Salmon have been marked in the Atlantic and North Sea, and of these most have entered the rivers close to where they were marked (Menzies, 1949). Others, however, have travelled from 100 to 1,600 miles before being recaptured.

In the course of these tagging experiments the fish are weighed, and some are killed for an examination of their stomachs. Many have had empty stomachs, having started their migratory fast, so it is not surprising that many of these fish when recaptured have lost weight in the interval between marking and capture. Calderwood and Menzies give examples of a $13\frac{1}{2}$ lb. fish losing $2\frac{1}{2}$ lb. in 77 days, a 15 lb. fish losing 4 lb. in 67 days, and a 12 lb. fish losing 2 lb. in 56 days.

Went (1949, 1951, 1953) has carried out a considerable

amount of tagging in Ireland; the work is still in progress but it justifies the tentative conclusion that Salmon move in from the sea at many places on the Irish coast. Once they reach Irish coastal waters the Salmon can and do travel long distances along the coast, and some may be on their way to rivers in Great Britain.

Marking experiments carried out in Scotland have shown that Salmon undertake local journeys as well as longer migrations. Many long journeys were recorded in the early Scottish experiments; for example fish marked on the west and north-west coasts of Scotland made journeys of as long as 410 miles: some were caught on the Yorkshire coast (about 300 miles) and another crossed the North Sea to Sogne fiord in Norway (about 400 miles).

After extensive Salmon tagging work had been done in Scotland, Menzies was able to show that Salmon from different localities covered varied distances in their coastal journeys. On the east coast and at the east end of the north coast of Scotland, the Salmon reaching the shallow waters do not travel any great distance before entering the rivers. On the other hand, Salmon entering the north-western coastal waters may travel considerable distances. A general picture of the movements of Salmon around Scotland shows that the Salmon move in from the oceans from the west or north-west, reach the west coast and then disperse to local rivers; if they reach the coast south of Barra Head they tend to move southwards; on the other hand, if they arrive on the Scottish coast north of the Butt of Lewis they will move northwards and eastwards in the coastal waters.

Dahl and Sømme (1942) in Norway have also carried out extensive tagging experiments, from which, again, two types of movement could be seen. Salmon caught inside the island belt (which runs for some distance along the coast of Norway) were near the end of their incoming journey and would not travel much further: but of those caught just outside the island belt some had a considerable way to go before reaching their destination.

We have scarcely begun to solve the problems of where the

Salmon feed in the sea. We do not know whether they congregate together on one feeding ground or are dispersed. We do not know what effect sea-feeding has on the future behaviour of the Salmon. I once suggested that those Salmon which are going to return to the river as grilse (p. 86) after a comparatively short time in the sea have feeding grounds comparatively near the coast, and that those which are to return as much older fish have feeding grounds at a distance many times greater. I know of no proof of this, though I still think it probable. Can it be supposed that all fish of any one year's smolt migration separate into groups once they reach the sea, some going to the nearby feeding grounds, others to feeding grounds further away, and yet another group to some very distant grounds? Will such a supposition explain why some fish spend as little as a year and a half in the sea, and others four years or more? Is it possible that all the fish of one year's smolt migration get the urge to return to the river to spawn simultaneously? If this is so, those fish which go to the nearby sea-feeding grounds must be the first (in age) to return; but the long-distance travellers might need a year or more to complete the return journey, and would thus be, say, $2\frac{1}{2}$ or 3 sea-years old on reaching the river. These questions cannot yet receive decisive answers. I do not myself believe that the time of return to the river is governed only by the characteristics of the Salmon's sea-feeding grounds: there must surely be some other factor, but what this is we do not know.

The speed at which a Salmon travels in the sea can be estimated from some of the results of the tagging experiments. In Sweden, Alm (1934) showed that small Salmon from Sweden and Northern Finland which have entered the Baltic between April and June, when about five inches in length, have travelled the distance of about 600 miles to the southern Baltic by October; unfortunately, it is not yet known whether these young fish are in a hurry to get to the main feeding grounds in the southern Baltic or whether they are moving southwards at a leisurely pace and perhaps stopping to feed at intervals on the way. The short inshore migrations will not give a good indication of rate of travel—just because the distances are short. Further, to draw

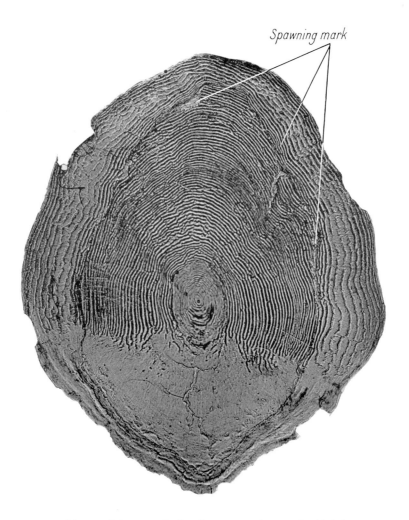

Spawning mark

Plate 7. Salmon scale showing a spawning mark. (*Irvine*)

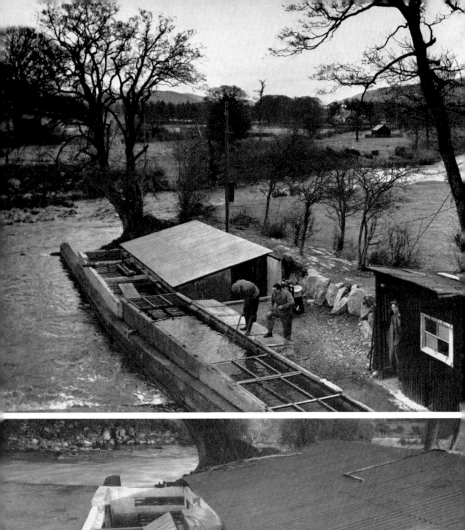

conclusions from the recoveries over longer distances involves several assumptions, some of which may be unwarranted—for instance, that the fish move away immediately they have been marked; that they take the shortest distance between two points; and that they are not helped or hindered by ocean currents. All estimates of speed based on tagging experiments lie between the extremes of 5 and 62 miles travelled per day. Menzies has suggested that distances of 1,000 miles may be covered at 25 miles per day; but he believes, as I do, that this figure may prove to be too conservative.

As mentioned in the previous chapter, it is possible, by scale-reading, to estimate the length of a fish at the end of each year of its sea-life. Calculations based on adult salmon scales from the Dee (fig. 9, p. 62) show that there is no significant difference in the length of the fish of various sea-age groups at the end of each sea-year of growth. There is nothing to suggest that these fish had not all been feeding in the same feeding ground; or, if in different grounds, then in grounds of similar quality. But comparison of the sea-growth of fish from different rivers may yet give some indication that they use different sea-feeding grounds. It would, of course, be essential that such a comparison should apply to simultaneous periods of sea-feeding.

We do not know how far its food determines the length of time a Salmon will spend in the sea before returning to the river; nor do we know what impels it to start this hazardous, and often final journey. The impulse may be indirectly related to internal changes, such as those in the development of the eggs and sperm, which in turn are dependent on the secretion of the endocrine glands. Yet it would be wrong to state categorically that Salmon will start to migrate when their gonads are in a certain developmental state; for some adult Salmon on arrival at the river are immature, with poorly developed gonads. Some of the fish

---

Plate 8 (*opposite*)
Above. A general view of the keeping tanks, observation tank and observation chamber. (*Russell Westwood, "Illustrated"*)

Below. The Observation Tank. (*Pilkington Bros.*)

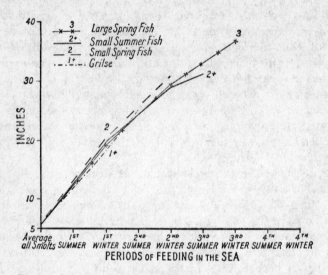

Fig. 9. Calculated yearly lengths of some sea-age groups of Welsh Dee Salmon. Large summer fish (3+ fish), and very large spring fish (4 fish) not shown

killed in the Welsh Dee, on the last day of December 1940, had gonads in a very undeveloped state and a great deal of reserve fat around their stomachs and in their mesenteries. The others, though also unspawned, had fully ripe gonads with no reserve mesenterial fat. Presumably the fat had been used up in the development of their gonads. These fish were not killed on the spawning grounds: indeed, there was every indication that they were all moving upstream. Yet some were due to spawn within a week or so, and the others not until the following November (Jones and King, 1946). It is not easy to believe that the impetus for the spawning migration of these fish was directly related to the attainment of a certain state of sexual development. At best it can be argued that the sexually mature were those that had had further to travel in the sea, and whose gonads had consequently had more time to develop.

A great deal of information about the changes which take place in the flesh, genitalia and digestive tract of the Salmon during its stay in fresh water was collected by Paton (1898) and his colleagues. One aspect of this detailed investigation which concerns us here is the change which takes place in ovary weight. Paton was able to show that during the period May to November there is a considerable increase in this weight. The average weight of the ovaries of fish caught in the estuary in May-June was 121 gms. This increased to 1,439 gms. in fish caught in November. The ovaries of fish caught in the upper water increased in weight from 263 gms. in June to 2,230 gms. in November. Hoek, Miescher, and Dahl and Sømme give similar figures for Salmon caught in the Lower Rhine, Upper Rhine and Norway respectively. It follows that the maturation of the gonads is seasonal, and independent of whether the Salmon is in the river or still in the sea. The December Dee fish referred to above must have represented the overlap of two distinct spawning years: this conclusion is supported by the absence of intermediates between the mature "late autumn" and the immature "early spring" fish, which happened to be travelling up the river at the same time. The observation throws no light at all on how or when the fish began to be affected by the urge to leave their feeding grounds in the sea and seek a river to spawn in.

This short and unsatisfactory chapter is little more than a confession of ignorance. British and Norwegian Salmon disappear completely from the time they leave the estuaries as smolts until the time when they re-enter coastal waters on their way to spawn. At such a moment in this period they may still have hundreds of miles still to go to re-enter their rivers, but become dedicated to this purpose and may begin their spawning fast. Of their life in the sea while they are still feeding and growing absolutely nothing is yet known. Nor can anything be certainly inferred from the knowledge that on the other side of the Atlantic some Salmon do not leave the Bay of Fundy or that in the brackish Baltic Sea some smolts have travelled 600 miles towards the Skagerrak in the six months after leaving their parent rivers. We do not yet know enough even to make intelligent guesses. And that for the present is that.

CHAPTER 5

THE HOMING INSTINCT AND
THE RETURN TO THE RIVER

DO Salmon in fact return to spawn in the river in which they were hatched? If so, how do they find their way back? Are they guided as well as driven by an inflexible and inherited instinct, or by a retentive memory of their youth? And, whatever its nature may prove to be, how specific is the guiding factor, and how variable? Are some Salmon not content till they have reached the same tributary, the same burn and even the same redd as they were hatched in? Will others, perhaps, accept any river they encounter on a wide stretch of coast?

These are fascinating questions to which all sorts of people have felt entitled to propose answers, for until quite recently speculation has ranged unhampered by any appreciable body of established fact. They are academic questions, in the sense that to answer them rightly would be to make a major contribution to biological science: but they are also practical questions, of importance to fishery management, for no one would wish to stock a river without some assurance of a return in fishable and marketable Salmon.

The only way to determine whether a Salmon is returning to its natural river is to mark or tag it as a young Salmon on its way down to the sea, and to recapture it on its return. According to Izaak Walton the return of Salmon had already been established in 1653 by "tying a riband or some known tape or thread" in the tail of smolts and catching them again when they came back to the same place ". . . usually six months after." But the classical tagging experiments carried out on the River Tay in 1905 and

1906 by the late P. D. H. Malloch of Perth, were, as far as I know, the first serious investigations carried out anywhere in the world. As published reports of this work are somewhat confusing, Mr. W. Malloch, B.Eng., the son of P. D. H. Malloch, has kindly allowed me to use his father's notes, which I summarise here.

Each smolt was held by one man in a specially prepared leather holder, while another tagged the fish by inserting a piece of german-silver wire in the thick portion of flesh in front of its dorsal fin. Both ends of the wire were then twisted into a loop. The 1905 marking started on 25 April and ended on 6 June. No marked fish were recaptured in 1905; marked fish were caught in the Tay from 1906 to 1909, and it is known that some marked fish were caught in other rivers, though not all the records are certain. In 1906 42 marked Salmon of average weight 6½ lb. were caught in the Tay; these were grilse having spent just over a year in the sea. In 1907, 57 marked Salmon were taken in the Tay after two years in the sea, and their average weight was 13 lb. In 1908, 9 marked Salmon of average weight 19¾ lb. were taken in the Tay; no marked Salmon was taken in 1909, but 3 marked and previously spawned sea-trout (called bull-trout in the Tay) were taken, proving that some of the smolts marked in 1905 must have been sea-trout smolts. Thus 111 marked fish were caught in the Tay, that is 1·7 per cent of the number marked.

Another crucial experiment on *Salmo salar* was carried out by White and Huntsman (1938 and White 1939) on the Apple River in Canada. The Apple River is a stream which opens into the Bay of Fundy; it is formed by two principal tributaries, the East Branch and the South Branch Rivers. The latter at that time had a normal run of Salmon which had spent only about one and a half years in the sea, and entered the river in late summer and autumn (grilse, see below). Until ten years before the experiment was started, the East Branch had a barrier across its mouth so that no Salmon could run up. A careful survey of the East Branch made by White and Huntsman before the start of the experiment showed that Salmon had not yet re-established themselves there after the breakdown of the barrier: no trace of adult or young Salmon was found in this tributary.

Eggs were taken from the River Restigouche, whose population of incoming fish was predominantly spring fish, *i.e.* they ran up the river in spring, after generally spending two to three years in the sea. An analysis of the normal incoming population of the Restigouche showed it to be composed of 10% grilse, 60% two-sea-year fish, and 30% three-sea-year fish. About 25,000 fry, none of which had grilse for parents, were eventually received from the Restigouche hatchery, and liberated into the East Branch of the Apple River. Their growth was observed throughout the two years they spent in the river as parr, and compared with that of the normal parr present in the South Branch. 3,252 smolts were taken in the East Branch trap about two years after the start of the experiment: 11 were of unknown origin, being three years old (probably immigrants from the South Branch) and the rest were two years old. Thus 13% of the planted fry had survived to the smolt stage. The 3,241 two-year-old smolts were marked by removal of the adipose fin, and released below the trap in 1934. In the autumn of 1935, 92 marked grilse entered the East Branch, and 6 the South Branch, and in the following year 5 two-year-old marked Salmon entered the East Branch and 1 the South Branch.

Some unequivocal conclusions may be drawn from these results. In the first place, since the fry from Restigouche Salmon eggs remained in the river as parr for only two years (in the Restigouche they would have migrated as three-year-old smolts), the time taken to develop into smolts (in this case at least) was determined by environmental factors and there was no observable inherited tendency. Secondly, since most of them returned as grilse in conformity with Apple River Salmon and unlike those of the Restigouche, the time of return also depends on environmental and not on hereditary factors. Thirdly, since the great majority of transplanted Salmon returned to the East branch in which they had lived as parr, they must somehow have remembered it and recognised it on their way up the Apple River. Fourthly, a significant minority of the transplanted Salmon, whether or not they recognised the entry to the East Branch, actually followed the established run up the South Branch. It follows that although a "memory" trace of the nursery stream may be a strong influence, it is not overriding: or perhaps they merely made a mistake.

It would, however, be going too far to say that this experiment, beautiful as it is, disproves the existence of a hereditary attraction for the parent stream. As in most marking experiments, the number of recoveries is too small for certainty; and, though it seems most unlikely, it is still possible to contend that the un-recovered fish were prowling hopelessly round the Bay of Fundy looking for the mouth of the Restigouche nearly a thousand miles away.

It will not be possible to deal in detail with all the North American marking and tagging experiments on *Oncorhynchus*. Foerster and Pritchard (1934), reporting on marked Pink salmon (*O. gorbuscha*) fingerlings at McClinton Creek 900 miles from Cultus Lake (British Columbia), found that the behaviour of these salmon was not in obvious accord with the parent-stream theory. Only 0·73% were recovered from 8,741 marked; of these, about six-tenths were recaptured in Canadian waters, the rest had strayed and were caught in American waters. In 1938, Pritchard reported somewhat more positive results and decided that there was a general tendency for Pink salmon to return to their natal stream (see also Pritchard, 1947).

The large-scale Cultus Lake experiment with Sockeye Salmon (*O. nerka*) carried out by Foerster and others (1940, 1954) showed that in spite of their being many strays there was a marked tendency for fish to return to their parent stream. In another experiment in which Foerster (1946) was trying to re-establish a run of Sockeye salmon in the River Fraser, the results were not then so favourable. In 1913 a rock-slide at and above Hell's Gate on this river had almost exterminated the large run of Sockeye salmon; in succeeding years large numbers of eggs and fry from the lower reaches of the Fraser River and from other rivers were planted in the Upper Fraser, but very few returned to spawn in this part of the river; in other words the salmon reared from eggs in the Upper Fraser River were on the whole not tempted to return to it, and a run to this area was not re-established

(Thompson 1945). Another similar experiment in 1922-26 was reported by Foerster (1934, 1936); in this instance eggs were planted in the Eagle River in the hope that a run of salmon would be established, but again few fish were caught there—a run had not been established by the transfer of eggs. Positive results were nevertheless obtained by Rich and Holmes (1929); they marked young Chinook salmon (*O. tschawytscha*) on the Columbia River over the period 1916-1927, and the results they obtained supported the "parent-stream" theory. It may be significant that where established populations have been marked the results have been positive, but many attempts to establish new runs have failed.

On the whole the results with *Oncorhynchus*, though more numerous, are less conclusive than those with *Salmo salar*. A possible reason for this is the greater technical difficulty of large-scale experiments in relatively undeveloped country. Another reason is that the Pacific genus *Oncorhynchus* is already split into at least five species with distinct but overlapping distributions and different habits, and this makes generalisation difficult. *Salmo salar*, on the other hand, is the same species from Cape Cod to Archangel and from Iceland to Portugal. So far as any conclusion is possible at this stage, it may be said that the drive to seek a river to spawn in is hereditary and common to migratory salmon everywhere, but that, in *Salmo salar* (and perhaps to a less and varying extent in the different species of *Oncorhynchus*) this drive is overlaid and guided by the individual memory of the peculiarities of a particular river and a particular tributary of that river. As has been pointed out above, White and Huntsman's experiment indicates that the preference of the Atlantic Salmon for spawning in its natal stream is a preference and not an overwhelming obligation. It is probably just this degree of tolerance which has enabled it to attain its present wide distribution without splitting up into distinct races or even species. It ensures that there will everywhere be some inter-breeding and that no natural calamity will permanently depopulate a suitable river: that is, it tends to maintain both genetic uniformity and continuity of distribution throughout the species' range.

Menzies (1939) claims that, "The existence of separate types of salmon in individual rivers is too well known to require either emphasis or proof." He bases this on the fact that the runs in some rivers commence in summer and autumn, and in others in spring, and that in some rivers the fish may be predominantly large while in others grilse may form the bulk of the catch. He continues, "Such variations might suggest special local stocks, but at the same time they may equally well be explained by some particular quality in each river which induces or entices a run of a certain type of fish at particular seasons of the year;" and "If each river did not have a local stock then the limitation of netting in any particular waterway would not be reflected in later years by the increase in the number of fish in that river." He quotes the rivers Aberdeenshire Dee, Wye, Conon and Ness as authentic examples of the beneficial effects of the restriction of netting. Huntsman, who has written extensively on this problem, condemns the use of the term "race" to define the various forms of salmon. He is of the opinion that the structural peculiarities which have been used to distinguish such "races" are being shown, one after the other, to be produced by differences in environment during the development of the individual, and are therefore not heritable. He says, "There is no definite clarification of the meaning of the word 'race' as applied to salmon." Professor Dahl on the other hand is prepared to use "race" without implying the question of heredity, that is, with no necessary implication of its being a "breed" or "lineage", which is the original meaning, and not easily kept out of mind. "No 'races' of Atlantic Salmon have yet been shown to be distinct through having a different inheritance." He also says, "It should not be assumed that I am against the homing conception, but I do not wish to accept it as established without clear evidence." Later Huntsman applies the term *ecotype* to different forms of salmon. An *ecotype* is ". . . the product of genetic response to a particular habitat, which may be recognised taxonomically or not according to the distribution of the particular habitat within the area of the species" (Cain, 1953).

These extracts from three acknowledged experts on Salmon

seem to imply a greater degree of difference of authoritative opinion than really exists, and they can all be reconciled if the use of ambiguous or tendentious words like *race*, *type* and *stock* is avoided. *Type*, though it seems at times an almost indispensable word, is a particularly dangerous source of misunderstanding. It is legitimate to use it in the form *ecotype* as strictly defined above: thus the assertion that salmon in the river Restigouche and the progeny of those transferred to the East Branch of the Apple River are distinct ecotypes, is a meaningful assertion, though it is probably a false one. Menzies, where he uses "types" in the first quotation above, appears to mean ecotypes in this sense, but it is most unlikely that spring-running and autumn-running fish in the same river are different *ecotypes,* and to say that they are different *types* seems to imply more knowledge than we possess. They are different certainly, as a tall man differs from a short, but tallness in man may result from the operation of either hereditary or environmental factors or, of course, both: and the division of mankind into short and tall types without knowledge of or regard for the causes of tallness, would be an entirely profitless exercise. In view of this confusion resulting from the misuse of terminology it might be best to call them local groups of Salmon.

To what extent are spring and autumn running hereditarily determined? The belief that spring runners transmit the habit to their offspring, condensed to the dogma "like begets like," has led to some expensive and, as far as is known, wholly unsuccessful attempts to induce or improve a spring run in a particular river by implanting eggs or fry from spring runners elsewhere. Mr. F. T. K. Pentelow, Chief Inspector of Salmon Fisheries for England and Wales, has told me, "I know of no authentic case where a spring run of salmon has been induced by the planting of spring-fish eggs. There are plenty of reports but none of them will stand up to scientific investigation, and there is no escaping the fact that in twenty years, between 1900 and 1920, the Wye produced a spring run without any artificial stocking whatever. I believe that before 1900 they only got summer fish."

To make the "like begets like" theory acceptable, it is necessary to assume that spring fish spawn exclusively with spring fish, and there is no evidence that this is true. In the Salmon observation tank I have seen grilse spawn with very large Salmon. It may be argued that this took place because conditions in the tank were not natural, and that the fish were overcrowded. The grilse could, however, have paired with another grilse, and the large fish could have paired with one more his size, but did not do so. And the spawning bed in the tank was in fact no more crowded than many natural spawning beds.

As will be seen in a later chapter, we have shown that male Salmon parr can become sexually mature and capable of fertilizing eggs and take part in the spawning act of the adults. I do not believe that a parr, the progeny of a spring-fish for example, can tell whether the adults in whose spawning he assists are spring or summer fish, nor do I think he would care. On the other hand, if it can be shown that fish of different sea-age groups, for example large spring-fish, small spring-fish, grilse etc., tend to spawn in different parts of the river, then it would be safe to assume that the parr inhabiting a particular spawning area were predominantly the progeny of one sea-age group. If, for example, grilse spawn in the smaller tributaries (as I believe they do), then the parr in these tributaries might easily be the progeny of grilse, in which case the male parr would not need to choose its adult co-spawners. Some indirect evidence that grilse tend to spawn in the smaller tributaries, where the food available to the resulting fry and parr may not be as good as that in the main stream, is provided by the number of grilse that have been three-year-old smolts (Menzies 1931, Hutton 1937). In rivers where the normal smolt age is two years, but with some few three-year-old smolts, most of these three-year-old smolts return as grilse, and, as has been shown earlier, three-year-old smolts have a much slower growth than the two-year-old smolts, and this presumably is the result of poorer feeding in the smallest burns.

There is, I think, some truth in the idea that, generally speaking, the grilse and some of the other smaller Salmon spawn in the tributaries, and that the large spring-fish spawn fairly high upstream in the main river, whereas the larger summer fish spawn further downstream, and the late or autumn fish spawn in the lower spawning beds. Is it not likely that it is the environment of the young Salmon during its parr years that determines the general course of its adult behaviour? This premise is wholly consistent with the Apple River experiment, where spring-fish young were planted in grilse environment and actually returned as grilse. The Shannon, which used to be a river into which big Salmon entered, provides a parallel example. When the spawning beds of the large fish were made unusable, the large fish presumably spawned in grilse water, and the parr developed grilse tendencies, with the result that the Shannon is now primarily a grilse river (Went, 1938, 1943, 1946, and 1955). The same may prove to be true of the River Bann (N. Ireland), where again most of the spawning grounds of the big fish in the main river have been destroyed, and the average weight of the fish caught is dropping considerably.

Finally, I shall cite the case of the River Ericht which was brought to my notice by Mr. W. Malloch of Perth, to whom I am indebted for the information given here. The Ericht, a tributary of the Tay in Scotland, at one time carried a large number of spring Salmon: three hundred spring Salmon were caught in one shot of the net in the Keith Pool. With the erection of Dam Dykes about a hundred years ago, a series of barriers for providing water-power to many mills in Blairgowrie, the spring run ceased. Several early efforts were made to build fish-passes over the barriers. Eventually in 1933 a series of fish-ladders were produced. In the same year re-stocking with spring-fish fry was started, and in spring, 1938, it was established beyond doubt that the stocking had been successful.

Mr. Malloch concludes, "Three points appear to have been firmly established:

  I. a spring-fish run has resulted from re-stocking with fry of spring fish;
  II. the spring run has become a permanency notwithstanding cessation of re-stocking in 1939;

III. the summer run has increased beyond all measure due to the
opening up of the weirs."

This was an example of the production of a spring-fish run from
the planting of spring-fish eggs. But they were planted in what
used to be an excellent spring-fish river, and so the young hatched
into a spring-fish parr environment; it was the effect of this
environment, I think, and not the fact that the eggs were from
spring fish, which determined the future behaviour of the Ericht
fish. I am sure that Mr. Malloch would have got the same results
had he planted summer-fish eggs.

From all the evidence so far given, it is safe to conclude that
the behaviour of the Salmon, in returning to spawn, is swayed to
a great extent by the environmental conditions in which the fish
lived as parr. For example, if for some reason a large spring
Salmon has to spawn in an environment where grilse normally
spawn, the progeny of this large spring fish will return to the river
as grilse. "Like begets like" is true only incidentally when the
young happen to be reared in an environment similar to that in
which their parents were reared as when, for example, English-
speaking parents usually beget English-speaking children. There
is no evidence at all of an inherited spring-running tendency.

There still remains the problem of how Salmon find their way
back to the parent river. Many attempts have been made to
solve it or at least to formulate some sort of consistent working
hypothesis. Powers (1939; Powers and Clark 1943) is of the
opinion that ". . . the guiding factors which are concerned in the
return of the Salmon are the physical and chemical characteristics
of the water to which Salmon are sensitive and so react and by so
doing do reach the spawning grounds, the parent stream."
According to Powers "In certain places, namely the aortic arch
and the carotid sinus, the blood-vessels of mammals have receptors
sensitive to pressure and to certain chemical substances, such as
oxygen and carbon dioxide tensions." He gives a list of various
investigators in this field, and points out that "in reptiles and
birds as well as mammals there are innervated structures
developed in connexion with the third branchial-arch artery and

an innervated pressure-receptor zone of the aorta. It is reasonable then to conclude that fish do possess these receptors in the regions of their gills." He showed that the Humpback salmon was sensitive to a gradient of salt-concentration in the water, and also showed that the alkali reserve in its blood is adjusted to the carbon dioxide tension of the water, provided that the latter is not changed too rapidly. He believes that these fish are very responsive to the composition of the sea-water in which they live. According to him, Pacific salmon in the sea drift with the currents, feeding all the time, but despite their drifting he does not believe that they move "outside the sphere of influence of the river water."

In answer to the question, "Why do salmon approaching sexual maturity return along definite paths to the spawning grounds?" Powers writes, "The ova and sperm-heads contain a protein (protamine) containing a large percentage of arginine. It requires a vast protein metabolism to obtain the necessary arginine. Protein metabolism and especially fasting—both necessary for the liberation of arginine from the muscular tissue of salmon—tends to produce acidosis of the blood, i.e. lower the alkali reserve of the blood. This is common knowledge. A salmon with low alkali reserve blood would find low carbon dioxide tension water more advantageous. We have produced evidence, if not proof, that fish do have receptors in their gills sensitive to carbon dioxide tension. Due to photosynthesis there must be a gradient of carbon dioxide from inshore to offshore waters. The salmon in its return is responding to the carbon dioxide tension gradient of a fresh-salt water gradient, at least inshore." Collins (1952) has demonstrated experimentally the repellant action of carbon dioxide on the upstream migration of the anadromous alewife (*Pomolobus pseudoharengus*) of Herring River, Massachusetts, U.S.A. When presented with waters having different amounts of free carbon dioxide, 72 per cent of the fish entered the channel with water of a lower free carbon dioxide content. Fontaine and Vibert (1952) believe salinity gradients to be used by Salmon for the location of the home stream.

Many others have written on this subject, but the theories on this point are supported by little evidence and are patently only adequate for those Salmon which remain within the influence of the parent rivers. The theory of Powers cannot, for instance, be applied to our sea-trout or any other fishes that feed as they migrate back to the river, and it leaves very nebulous the nature of the "influence" on which it basically relies.

In 1880, Frank Buckland suggested that Salmon were assisted by their power of smell to find their way in the ocean, and also to find their parent river. He described the olfactory organ as a "beautiful bit of mechanism," and pointed out how exquisitely it is adapted to smelling in water. He adds: "Doubtless, to the fish, each river has got its own smell; taste or flavour it has hitherto been called, but this I think is a wrong expression, as a salmon's tongue has hooks upon it and is not so sensitive as the tongue of land animals; in fact, it is more an organ of prehension than taste. When the salmon is coming in from the sea he smells about till he scents the water in his own river. This guides him in the right direction, and he has only to follow up the scent, in other words 'to follow his nose', to get into fresh water, that is if he is in a travelling humour. Thus a salmon coming up from the sea into the Bristol Channel would get the smell of water meeting him. 'I am a Wye salmon', he would say to himself. 'This is not the Wye water; it's the wrong tap, it's the Usk. I must go a few miles further on', and he gets up steam again!"

It is becoming increasingly clear that Buckland, more than 70 years ago, was thinking on the right lines. More recently, Hasler and Wisby (1951) are attempting the difficult task of proving that there is, in the water of every river, a characteristic odour to which young salmon become accustomed, and that on their return migration they recognise this odour, orient themselves, and so pursue it to their parent stream. As Hasler (1954) points out, three distinct questions need affirmative answers.

a. Do streams have characteristic odours to which fish can react? What is the nature of such odours?
b. Can salmon discriminate between such odours?
c. Can salmon retain odour impressions from youth to maturity?

Ingenious preliminary experiments by Hasler and Wisby showed that it was possible to train a group of North American minnows to discriminate between the smells of two Wisconsin creeks. After being trained, the olfactory tissue of these trained fish was destroyed and they were no longer capable of making the distinction. The retentive power of the trained minnows lasted for several days, and it was found that young fish remembered for longer periods than older fish. Having got so far, Hasler and Wisby then decided to try to find some artificial substance to which young salmon could be conditioned, and which could be put in a stream to attract these salmon as they moved back from the sea. It was decided after many experiments to use for this purpose a very dilute solution of morpholine (diethylenimide oxide). Field tests are now in progress to determine whether salmon fry and fingerlings which have been conditioned to morpholine can be decoyed to a stream other than that of their birth, upon their return to fresh water as adult migrants. In 1953 another interesting experiment was conducted by Wisby and Hasler (1954) to find out to what extent homing salmon, which had actually reached the main stream, were dependent on odours in determining which tributary, they would swim up. In this instance sexually ripe Coho salmon were caught in two tributaries of the Issaguah River in Washington. They were placed in tanks and returned to the main river below the point at which it divided into the two tributaries, so that they would once again have to run upstream and choose their tributary. In one half of the fish so returned, the nasal sac was plugged with cotton-wool, and these fish were therefore not able to perceive odours (the perception of odours by any other sense, such as the skin chemical receptors, is apparently not sufficiently sensitive to be affected by the smell of the tributaries). The result of the experiment was clear-cut:— "The great majority of normal fish selected again the stream of first choice, while the plugged-nose fish returned in nearly random fashion" (Hasler, 1956). This suggests that the olfactory sense is of major importance as a navigational aid to migrating fishes.

The olfactory sense of Coho salmon was tested by Brett and

MacKinnon (1954), following their discovery (1952) that extremely dilute odours produced from human skin, when placed in a stream up which fish were migrating, resulted in a marked decrease in the rate of upstream migration of the Coho and Spring salmon. That human odours in water do affect salmon has been known for some time. Professor Thompson from Washington, when visiting our Salmon observation tank, told me of some observations he had made in Alaska on this point—how salmon congregating on a spawning ground would disperse rapidly if a bear put its paw in the water upstream of the fish. Brett and MacKinnon carried out their tests at a fish-pass where ascending fish could be seen leaping from one basin in the pass to another and the test substances were put into the water at times when the rate of migration of the fish had become constant; the substances were added to the water at the next basin upstream in the fish-pass. Such things as aniseed oil, salmon milt, Brasso, shark repellent, human hand, bear's paw, lactic acid, phenol and various other substances with characteristic odours were used. In all, 54 substances were tested, and care was taken to ascertain that these were not contaminated by contact with the hands of the experimenters. Of the 54 odours tested, only the odours from human skin, bear's paw, deer foot, dog's paw, and sea-lion meat produced a significant change in the migration-rate. This change was characterised by a complete halt in the upstream migration for at least five minutes; then the fish swam about showing what may be called an "alarm-reaction" by swimming back and forth across the pool, some even dropping back into the next pool. The next five minutes was a period of alertness when the fish were very timid, and then behaviour became normal and the original rate of migration was reattained in about fifteen minutes after the addition of the odour. These experiments also confirm that salmon have an acute and discriminative sense of smell, and that they can detect and respond to the smell of potential predators. It is quite likely that they perceived all the other odours, but did not associate them with danger in that particular situation and so did not respond. This, of course, would account for the movement of salmon upstream into polluted areas of some of our rivers, and the mortality resulting from such behaviour. If the fish recognized the odours as dangerous they could, on first detecting the pollution, turn back downstream out of the danger area. Unfortunately this does not usually happen.

It has also been suggested (White, 1934) that the presence of fish in a river may influence the entry of other fish: thus the smell of salmon parr in a river might attract the returning adults. But if so, one would have expected the salmon studied by Brett and MacKinnon to have responded more positively to such fish derivatives as salmon ova, testes, milt, blood and skin, which were used in this experiment. They gave no response to these substances, nor to a series of substances which may have resembled the excretory products of fish nitrogen metabolism. Of course it may still be that White is right, and that the attraction of the salmon parr resides in substances not included in tests mentioned above.

Having found the estuary of the river which they will ascend, the Salmon may spend a considerable time in it waiting until water conditions are suitable or favourable for their upstream migration. We do not know what these conditions are; I think that there may be a constellation of factors related to the height of the water in the river, the temperature of the water, the colour of the water, and possibly other factors not perceptible to man. These factors will not be the same for any two rivers, nor will they be similar in any one river two years in succession. It may be that the upstream migration is assisted by the use of the lateral-line in detecting water movements. There are many instances of the effect of temperature on the movements of Salmon fry and adults (Sullivan 1954), and Hayes (1946) showed how temperature determined the position of speckled trout in two lakes in Nova Scotia.

Efforts have been made to induce Salmon to move upstream out of tidal water by making artificial freshets or spates. Huntsman (1948) set up a dam in the dry summer of 1942 and produced freshets by opening it: he found that short successive freshets in the latter part of July brought Salmon up, but he was unable to decide whether the increased current or the consequent dilution of the estuarine water was the effective stimulus. The experiment was repeated during the wet summer of 1943 with even less definite results. Hayes (1953) followed on this preliminary work of Huntsman with a large-scale experiment, the results of which showed that the artificial freshets that produced the best movements of fish were a pair on successive nights; the first would bring the fish some distance up the estuary and the second would bring them into fresh water. Single freshets, he found, can move fish which happen to be at the head of the tide into fresh water, but are not by themselves able to move fish into the estuary; maybe they would succeed if worked with suitable tide and winds. On the other hand, Hayes found that if the river level was cut down (that is, the reverse of a freshet), this also might act as a stimulus in moving fish, and might prove quite as successful as an artificial freshet if correctly timed. Hayes also found that Salmon tended to move out of tidal waters into fresh water at dusk, and that the changes of water temperature seemed to have little effect in initiating the upstream runs of the fish.

Large natural freshets are supposed to initiate a major run of fish into a river. Menzies (1931) describes how in dry weather, grilse which were held up in tidal waters, moved up the estuary just ahead of the tide, and fell back with the tide as it ebbed; but during a spate tidal movements were ignored, and the fish entered the estuary and moved directly and rapidly upstream.

Ward (1939), who has spent many years observing the migrations of the Sockeye (*Onchorhynchus nerka*), believes that it is the environmental conditions in the river that determine the upstream movement of this fish when adult. One of the major influences is the current; in his opinion *rheotropism*, the tendency to swim against a current (Chapter 2, p. 36), explains why the Sockeye in estuaries (unlike Menzies' Salmon, referred to above) move upstream with a falling tide, and move downstream again with a rising tide—but a smaller distance than they move upstream. Eventually they pass out of tidal influence and, once in the stream, continue their ascent against the current. They cannot do this continuously owing to the need for rest, especially in warm weather; so-called resting pools are found in all good salmon rivers. According to Ward the Sockeyes rest at night and are most active in the early hours of the morning. Light has some influence on upstream migration. Ward gives a striking instance of this: fish were moving unhesitatingly up a fish-ladder in great numbers until the sun's rays (appearing over a ridge) illuminated the water in the ladder. As soon as this happened, the fish stopped moving until late afternoon, when most of the light was reflected off the surface and the water was darker. It would have been of considerable interest had Ward taken note of the temperature-changes involved. According to Menzies, it is a recognized fact that low temperatures also adversely affect movements of Salmon over fish-ladders. At temperatures below 42°F (about 5°C) an obstacle in the river may be impassable, though fish move over it easily when the water is warmer. It may also be true that exceptionally high temperatures make obstacles impassable.

What percentage of the smolts leaving the river return as adults? Estimates vary according to the basis of calculations, which in all cases is extremely shaky. Some say that a pair of Salmon will produce five adult fish, others say only three. It is obvious that, if the total numbers of *Salmo salar* are stable over a long time, two breeding fish produce on the average two offspring which survive to breed—no more and no less. This truism is not however applicable over a short period or over a limited part of the species' range. Despite all the marking and tagging experiments I am afraid that any figures suggested can only be guesses based on questionable estimates of the survival-rate at each stage in the life-cycle.

What percentage of eggs are fertilized in a normal spawning of adult Salmon? It is not surprising that there has been little agreement on this point, as it is not easy to make accurate counts without much preparation and knowledge of the exact position of the eggs in the river. When redds were opened by Calderwood (1931), he found few, if any, dead eggs, but concluded that hatching under natural conditions is not as successful as that in a hatchery. Some have guessed a good natural hatch to be in the region of 40 per cent, but this is certainly much too low. White (1942), who opened up new salmon beds and removed the eggs, obtained a 78 per cent hatch; and it is reasonable to suppose that a higher percentage would have hatched if the eggs had not been moved. In the Salmon observation tank we obtained hatches ranging from 97·4 per cent to 98·6 per cent; admittedly circumstances here were nearly ideal—but, except in the worst conditions of overcrowding or flood damage, I would not expect a natural hatch to be lower than 75 per cent. Hobbs (1937) gives data of the survival of Quinnat salmon, brown and rainbow trout in New Zealand. In undisturbed redds the hatch of Quinnat Salmon was over 97%, and of brown trout over 95%, while the losses shown by rainbow trout were "not inconsistent with the results obtained in the case of brown trout under similar circumstances."

Some figures are available for the survival of planted eggs and fry up to smolt stage. In the Apple River experiment, 13 per cent of the planted fry had reached the smolt stage. Pritchard (1947) kept a record of the spawning of *O. gorbuscha* in McClinton Creek and found that 76·2 per cent to 93·1 per cent of the potential hatch (i.e. eggs carried upstream in salmon) were lost between the time of upstream migration and the entry of the fry into the sea. Foerster and Ricker (1953) estimated that three smolts were produced by every adult female fish (*O. kisutch*).

The percentage of smolts that survive to return as adults is even more conjectural. I have often heard it said that of a thousand smolts only two return as adults. In the Tay marking experiments 1·7 per cent and 3·1 per cent returned or, rather, were caught; in the Apple River work about 3 per cent returned, and in many other experiments the returns have been even less. But combining the most favourable of the figures available, each breeding pair would only need to produce about 1,000 fertile eggs to maintain the population. And certainly they usually produce far more.

Foerster (1954) has published much useful information on the subject. Over the period 1927 to 1944, he obtained from the Cultus Lake experiments data of the mean length and weight of the smolts migrating seawards, and the number of adults which returned to the river. He was able to estimate the number that escaped capture and were able to spawn. He found that a good spawning year (that is the presence of a large number of fish on the spawning beds) does not always result in good returns later when the progeny from such spawnings return to the river. If there are too many fish on the spawning beds, there is *overcutting*, and the eggs laid by one female are disturbed and wasted as another female spawns in the same spot. In the event of an exceptionally good hatch of young there may not be enough food available, and the stock suffers. It is also just possible that, should these large numbers of young reach the sea, then the food in the neighbouring oceanic feeding grounds may not be enough to meet the demand of such large numbers. According to Foerster, if conditions in any of these three respects are unfavourable, serious loss in production results. Dealing with data from over 20,000,000 smolts, he was able to show statistically that the size of smolts at migration was inversely related to their number, and that during the seaward migration, the mortality among the smaller smolts was greater than among the larger. When the spawning season was exceptionally good, large numbers of smolts were produced, but their average size was low; so he concludes that it is better not to have an exceptionally good spawning season, as the eventual result in return of adult fish is poorer than that of a normal seaward migration. It is perhaps as well to be cautious in taking these results with *Oncorhynchus* as being applicable to *Salmo salar*.

When they first reach the river the Salmon are in good condition and very silvery. Their flesh is firm, and as great a store of nourishment as the body can carry has been accumulated. According to Paton (1898), this supply of material is enough to produce the mature ovaries and testes, and also to supply the energy necessary for the fishes' arduous and energetic upstream migration. He seems to think that as the fish have acquired such a store, there is no reason why they should feed in the river. Naturally the longer they stay in the river the more of this store is used up, so that for culinary purposes the best Salmon is one caught in early spring either in the estuary or soon after its entry into the river; a late-running fish with fairly mature gonads has a lower food-value than a spring fish. The morphological changes which take place as the fish approaches sexual maturity will be dealt with later.

Salmon do not feed in the river; large numbers of Salmon stomachs have been examined and found empty or with slight traces of sea-food in them. It is just as well that they do fast, for the fish population of almost any Salmon river would be completely depleted if the incoming Salmon were as voracious in the river as they are in the sea.

Why, then, do Salmon take anglers' flies, spoons, lures, shrimps, minnows, etc.? Who can tell? It could be anger, or curiosity; I have seen a Salmon in the observation tank snap at and break a twig the diameter of my little finger—he looked angry, he may have been angry; on the other hand, I have watched Salmon in the tank ignoring a bunch of succulent worms which were dangled on and in front of their snouts, and refusing to be interested by the gaudiest Salmon-flies. It is certainly not true, as has often been suggested, that Salmon in the river take food and "squeeze the goodness out" without swallowing the solid matter. The reality of their fast is indicated by the loss in weight of their muscles, which may be as much as 25 per cent.

Many investigators who have long studied the scale-markings of Salmon are convinced that not only do scales furnish a means of determining the age of a Salmon, but also enable the investigator to tell in which river the fish was reared (Ward, 1939). Menzies (1949) claims "that when the examination of the parr area has been possible, [adult] fish marked on the west coast of Scotland and recaptured in rivers on the East coast or in Norway can be identified as natives of the river in which they were finally taken." My own observations, however, indicate that he is over-confident. I once thought it conceivable that a careful survey of parr-scales from various rivers might furnish some rule for identifying the river of origin of the adult fish by examination of the parr centre on the adult scale (Jones, 1949). I thought that there might be such a thing as an average or typical parr-scale for each river (all scale samples being taken from the same area on the body of the fish), and that such an average scale might have a distinctive number of rings in each of the seasonal bands, i.e. first and second summer band, and first and second winter band, and that the ratio of these numbers might also be used for identification purposes.

The following table gives the results of such counts for the scales from about 3,000 fish; the figures are averages of ring counts from about twenty to thirty normal scales from each fish:

River	1st Year		2nd Year	
	Summer	Winter	Summer	Winter
Dart	5·8	3·8	11·0	*
Taw	6·0	3·5	11·1	2·9
Severn	7·0	2·0	12·0	5·0
Teme	10·2	4·3	13·3	*
Wnion	4·5	2·7	8·8	2·7
Seiont	5·6	2·6	6·1	3·0
Conway	5·8	2·9	10·7	3·2
Esk	5·0	3·1	7·9	2·8
Dee (Welsh)	5·1	2·9	10·7	3·4
Ure	5·2	3·3	11·2	2·7
Eden	7·5	3·5	9·1	*
Derwent	4·7	2·9	8·8	2·9
Tees	4·0	3·0	11·6	3·0
Tyne	4·1	2·6	8·4	3·4

* Band incomplete

It is seen that these counts, except for those of the River Teme, were of no critical value for individual rivers. Nevertheless the scales can be divided into four well-defined groups:

a. The River Teme scales, on which there was an average of 10·2 rings in the first summer, 4·3 in the first winter, 12·0 in the second summer and 5·0 in the last winter.

b. The Dart, Taw, Severn and Eden scales, which all have a mean of nine or more first-year rings; in the Eden fish the second-year rings were less numerous than those on the scales of fish from the other three rivers.

84

c. The Seiont, Conway, Dee, Esk, Ure and Derwent scales, on which there were more than eight but less than ten first-year rings, with a considerable variation in the number of second-year rings.

d. The Wnion, Tyne and Tees scales, on which the number of the first-year rings varied from a mean of 6·6 to 7·2.

Unfortunately these groups of rivers are not entirely geographical; for example group *b* contains southerly and northerly rivers, *c* and *d* mid-country and northerly rivers. It is probable that these variations are, in large part at least, dependent upon such factors as temperature and food-supply. And even within a single large watershed there is a great variation in the number of rings in each seasonal band on scales of fish from the same river.

The fish that enter our rivers can, from the examination of their scales, be classified into sea-age groups. These sea-age groups are defined by the length of time the fish has spent in the sea before starting its fasting journey back to the river. The age of the fish as a smolt is disregarded in this classification, so that the actual age of the fish is not given; for example, two fish which have spent the same length of time in the sea may have a total age differing by one or more years—one may have spent one year in the river as a parr and the other three years, yet both are put into the same *sea*-age group. This is a very convenient way of classifying incoming Salmon, but, most unfortunately (though perhaps inevitably) the sea-age groups have been labelled with names which were already in use before improvements in scale-reading technique permitted a fairly precise determination of sea-age. The consequence is that these names now have two meanings: and, though both meanings usually apply to the same set of fish, the correspondence is not sufficiently absolute to avoid confusion and misunderstanding. For example, the old and legitimate meaning of a *spring fish* is a Salmon which is either caught in the river or its approaches in the spring, or seen to be running then. For the scale-reader, a spring fish is one whose scales show that it was feeding and growing at the reduced (or winter) rate when it left its sea-feeding grounds and started its spawning fast. The majority of spring fish are doubtless spring fish in both senses, but some which are spring fish to the scale-reader either arrive so late that they run up with summer fish, or so early that they may be confused with late autumn-runners of the previous year (winter fish, see below). *Grilse* is an older and even more dubious term. Before a committee of the House of Commons in 1884 a Mr. Johnstone is reported as saying: "The grilse is a much less fish in general, it is much smaller at the tail in proportion and it has a much more swallow tail, much more forked; it is smaller at the head, sharper at the point of the nose, and generally the grilse is more bright in the scale than the salmon." (Day, 1887). An etymological dictionary of the Scottish language gives *grilse*, "a salmon not fully grown as the term is generally understood, although some view it as a distinct species." The Oxford English Dictionary says it is "the name given to a young salmon on its first return to the river from the sea and is retained during the same year." This last meaning is the most definite and on paper the most acceptable: but in practice grilse is often used to describe any small Salmon—and certainly sea-trout have been described as grilse and *vice versa*. This last error possibly accounts for the superstition that grilse survive spawning and return as Salmon. This is without foundation; the percentage of grilse which survive spawning is no larger than the percentage of Salmon. The only satisfactory definition of a grilse is a Salmon which returns to the river for the first time after having spent a little more than one year in the sea.

The accepted definitions of sea-age groups in current use are as follows:

a. *Grilse, sea-age group 1 +*
   Has spent one complete year and part of a summer in the sea, and is returning in mid or late summer. Scales show one sea summer band of rings, one sea winter band (together making one year) and part of a second summer.
b. *Small spring fish, sea-age group 2*
   Has spent two complete years in the sea and is returning

generally in spring. Scales show one summer, one winter, one summer, and one winter band of sea-rings.

c. *Small summer fish, sea-age group 2+*
One sea-year older than a grilse; thus scales show extra winter and summer band of rings (Plate 6, p. 53).

d. *Large spring fish, sea-age group 3*
One sea-year older than the small spring fish.

e. *Large summer fish, sea-age group 3+*
Two sea-years older than grilse.

f. *Very large spring fish, sea-age group 4*
Two sea-years older than the small spring fish.

g. *Very large summer fish, sea-age group 4+*
Three sea-years older than grilse.

All the above terms refer to virgin or maiden fish. Salmon which are returning to spawn for the second time (or, more rarely, a third or fourth time) are termed previous spawners and designated P.S., their sea-age being read up to the sea-age at the time of the first spawning; for example, if the fish had first spawned as a grilse, it would be designated 1+S.M.+ (S.M. standing for spawning mark). It is possible to guess from the scale approximately how long fish spend in the sea between spawnings; those that stay six months or less are called short-absence fish, those that stay longer (say six months to a year) long-absence fish. I must stress that these terms are only estimates based on the number of rings present on the scales between the spawning marks, and are unsatisfactory. The lapse of time represented by a ring is not established and probably varies from fish to fish. The scale-reader's terminology is also unsatisfactory in other respects. The use of the terms "large" and "small" is unfortunate. One would expect a small summer fish to be smaller than a large summer fish, but a small summer fish can weigh as much as 25 lbs. and a large summer fish only 15 lbs.

In 1939, a few years after starting to read Salmon scales, I suggested an alternative terminology, but now I am not at all certain that this was any improvement on the old one. I am sure, however, that misunderstanding would be much reduced if we dispensed with the present verbal classification and consistently referred to the sea-age groups by numbers as follows: a grilse=a 1+ fish (a one-plus fish): a small spring fish=a 2 fish: a small summer-fish=a 2+ fish, and so on. When it is necessary to refer to the river life of a fish, this may be represented without ambiguity by a figure preceding that for the sea-age, thus a small summer fish which had migrated as a two-year-old smolt may be designated 2.2+ (spoken of as a two-two-plus fish).

It is not always realised that Salmon may enter some of our rivers at any time in the year; though of course in every river there are peak periods where the numbers moving in are relatively great. A spring-fish river (or early river) such as the Welsh Dee, has a big run of salmon in March and April, whereas some rivers, such as the Cumberland Derwent, have practically no fish running up in spring, and the main upstream migration in summer; in some rivers this run does not take place until autumn.

Analyses of the scales of Welsh Dee Salmon taken during the fishing season over a period of twenty years, show clearly how the various sea-age groups run into the river and reach the peak of their run at different times of the year, and that 90 per cent of the smolts leave the river as two-year-olds (Jones, 1953). Figure 10. p. 89, gives an analysis of the monthly distribution of 3-fish, 2-fish, 2+fish and 1+fish (grilse) over the period 1937-1951 and shows how much information can be obtained from scale-reading. The fish were taken by net in the estuary, and at Chester, or by rod several miles upstream from Chester. Of all the 3-fish sampled, 40·7 per cent were taken between March 15th and 31st, and most of these (67·3 per cent) were taken by rod: 37·6 per cent of the remainder were taken in April and again most of these were rod-caught. During these two months 3-fish were more numerous than 2-fish; and, as most of the 3-fish caught in March are rod-caught fish, there can be little doubt that many of these had actually started moving upstream before the fishing season opened on 15 March. A third of the total number of 2-fish sampled was caught in March, but most of them were taken by net at Chester even further down-stream in tidal waters. Nearly 40 per cent of the total of 2-fish were taken in April, and more than half of these

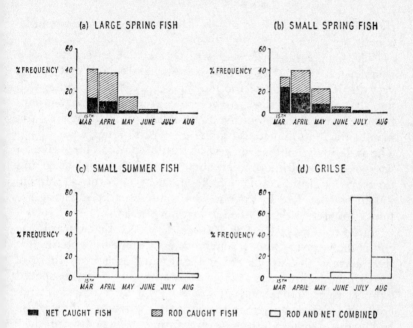

FIG. 10. Percentage monthly distribution of large spring fish. (3 fish) small spring fish (2 fish), small summer fish (2+ fish), and grilse (1+ fish) in the Welsh Dee 1937–51

were taken by rod; these, too, therefore reach the peak of their run in early April. 2 + fish generally arrive in the river at the end of April, and reach the peak of their run in May; these in turn are followed by the 1 + fish (grilse) which may start to appear in June, and reach the peak of their run in July. From a consideration of these figures it is evident that the classification into sea-age groups of the fish caught over a period of years permits the construction of a fairly clear picture of a river's in-season population; and it is an excellent way of finding out whether major changes take place in it. Such changes can often be related to ecological factors operating in earlier years, such as pollution, drainage, poor spawning seasons, droughts, etc. And, of course, the Welsh Dee investigations showed that if the fishing season was opened on

89

the first of March instead of the 15th, many more fish would be caught.

The Cumberland Derwent may be taken as an example of a summer-fish river. Scale investigations have shown that only a very small proportion of the incoming migrants are spring fish, and that 1 + fish (grilse) are generally the dominant age-group, forming more than half of the total fish sampled, though 2+fish may be the most numerous fish in other years (Jones, 1950, 1953). The scale investigations of Menzies and McFarlane have given a very great deal of information about Scottish Salmon; these and the works of Hutton on Wye Salmon, and Went on Irish salmon, should be consulted by anyone who is interested in pursuing the subject in greater detail (see bibliography, p. 173).

Scale-reading of the Derwent scales showed that towards the end of the year, in October and November, some fish entering the river have scales which are not distinguishable from those of spring fish, as they have at their edges a band of narrowly spaced (winter) rings (Jones, 1953). The edges of these scales are not eroded, as they would be in October and November, if these fish had actually entered the river in spring. These fish produce terminological chaos unless those who rely on the scale-readers' classification always remember that it is based on "sea-age", which is not necessarily predictive of the time of running up the river. Among the Welsh Dee fish killed by pollution in 1940, similar late-running fish were found to be of two types physiologically and represent the overlap of two spawning years though their scales were indistinguishable (page 62). We (Jones and King, 1946) called these fish collectively "winter fish". Huntsman (1933) reports that, in 1932, permission was given for Salmon fishing to take place in St. John Harbour from the first of November, and as a result, about twenty hundredweight of Salmon were caught during that month. These fish were very fat and quite immature sexually. Huntsman finds no reason to believe that they would have spawned before the following October. They were, for the most part, female grilse, but as they were caught so late in the season were, in fact, a bit older in sea-age. Went (1949) has found similar late-running fish in Irish rivers, the large fish having scales which are indistinguishable from those of large spring fish, and the smaller ones scales indistinguishable from those of fresh-run small spring fish, though both these types were heavy in spawn. He also found that there were very early runs of spring fish in which the gonads were immature. He suggests that the late-running mature fish are the same "type" as the summer fish, and the early immature fish are of the same "type" as very early spring fish. However, his findings seem closely parallel to ours in the Dee, in that these very late (or very early) runners are of two physiologically distinct sets whose scales are indistinguishable and of the spring fish type. It seems safer to group them together in the provisional category of "winter fish" till we know more about them. In so doing, it must be made clear that winter fish is not a class recognisable by the scale-reader; it is based on behaviour. The use of such a term is an additional reason, if one were needed, for abandoning the verbal labels of the scale-reader's sea-age classification in favour of the numerical.

CHAPTER 6

THE SALMON IN THE RIVER—I

The Spawning of the Adults

BY October most of the adult Salmon have assembled in pools not far from where they are going to spawn. The spring fish, making a relatively leisurely passage up-stream, have been overtaken and passed by the grilse, which arrive later in the river and usually spawn in the remotest redds of all. The late autumn fish are believed to prefer beds nearer to tidal waters than the spring fish.

By spawning time considerable changes have taken place in the appearance of the Salmon. They are no longer the magnificent silvery fish that entered the river: the females are now generally quite dark in colour, and the males reddish. The head of the males has undergone a pronounced transformation to produce the *kype*. This is formed by a prolongation of the lower jaw, which is now hooked at its end (Plates 12 a and b, p. 129; Figure 11, p. 94), the hook fitting into a socket on the equally prolonged upper jaw. The front teeth are enlarged, with the result that the fish has a rather snarling look.

Tchernavin (1938) has studied the changes which take place in the skull as spawning-time nears. He distinguishes five stages. At first, on the sea feeding-grounds, the skull has long narrow teeth which are particularly narrow at their bases and are fastened firmly on to the jaw-bones. The premaxillary bones are short and wide posteriorly. When the Salmon are moving in towards the shore, these teeth are shed, but immature teeth are to be found lying horizontally in the connective tissue of the jaws, with their tips pointing into the mouth. In the third stage, (in the river in the case of spring fish), the gonads are developing, and the immature teeth are developing and gradually fusing to the jaw-bones. The cartilaginous front end of the jaws and all the jaw-bones are elongating. In the fourth stage, the teeth are longer, broader at their base, curved, and united to the bones (and probably function as threat weapons). The lengthened premaxillaries reach beyond the rostrum. And finally, after spawning, the breeding teeth degenerate and are replaced by newly-grown feeding teeth. The length of the jaw-bones and rostrum diminishes and the skull slowly returns to its Stage 1 form.

In addition to the changes in the form of the skull, the skin of both sexes, though most markedly of the male, becomes thick and spongy so that the scales are deeply embedded in it and cannot easily be removed without making a nasty wound. The erosion of the scales, which will ultimately leave the spawning mark, is already far advanced in spring fish. Much of the muscle protein and fat has been used up to form the gonads, the flesh is less pink than it used to be, and the fish is in a poorer general condition than when it arrived in the river.

Greene (1915, 1919 and 1921), who studied the changes that take place in the flesh before and during spawning, has shown that in the Pacific King salmon the muscle protein is reduced to about 70 per cent and the fat to between 20 per cent and 2 per cent of the amounts present in fish fresh from the sea, but meanwhile the weight of the gonads may have increased about five-fold. The ovaries are full of eggs and fill up most of the body-cavity of the female, whilst in the male the mature testes are a pair of large white bodies, slightly wider in front, which run almost the length of the body-cavity. The testes have wide ducts which unite near the termination of the urethra, and open on the urinogenital papilla, which lies in the cloaca (the vent). The milt or sperm is a thick white fluid containing vast numbers of spermatozoa. A fully ripe ovary has only a very thin wall; this ruptures, shedding the eggs into the body-cavity, whence they are forced out through the enlarged cloacal papilla. The eggs in the body-cavity are soft and not very round. Once extruded they are

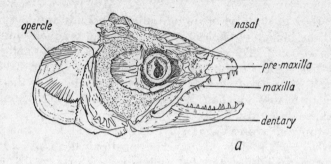

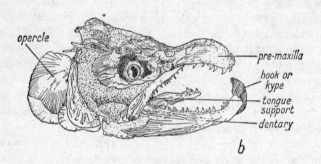

FIG. 11. The skull of the Salmon

a. Female in the sea; male very similar at this stage.
b. Male on the spawning grounds.

sticky and adhere to whatever they touch; they absorb water rapidly and become spherical.

The diameter of the eggs after extrusion is between 0·2 and 0·3 inches. It is not certainly determined whether their size is dependent on the size of the mother—a point which will be taken up again in a later chapter. The number of eggs produced by a female Salmon varies considerably. Day estimated that the Atlantic Salmon produces about 900 eggs per pound of body-weight. We found (Jones and King, 1946) that the number of eggs was 7,750 in an 18½-lb. fish and 8,470 in an 11-lb. fish, which means 418 and 770 eggs per lb. respectively. In this size-range, therefore, the total number of eggs carried by the female was not closely dependent on her size. The accepted average is, however, 650 to 700 eggs per pound of body-weight. Salmon eggs kept in the body-fluid will remain viable for quite a long time; Day records an instance where eggs were found to retain their vitality and capacity for fertilization in a Salmon that had been dead for at least two hours. When mixed with excess of river water the sperm dies almost at once, but if kept in the fluid extruded with the eggs at a temperature of slightly over 0°C it will remain active for several days (Ellis and Jones, 1939). It is not known how long it will remain active in this fluid if kept at higher temperatures; presumably it survives longer than in water.

The spawning behaviour of Salmon has been a subject of interest for a great many years, and many mutually contradictory descriptions have been published. This is not surprising, for Salmon spawn in fast-moving water in November and December, a time of the year when the light is poor, the water usually dirty, and accurate observations not easy to make. Before the last war I spent many hours both by day and by night on Salmon spawning-beds in rivers without making any useful observations. Occasionally quite a lot can be seen from a conveniently situated bridge, but never enough to ensure a correct interpretation unless the observer already knows the whole story.

Scrutiny of the literature on this topic discloses a number of erroneous beliefs: that the male Salmon digs a nest in which the female lays her eggs; that the female Salmon passes out her eggs as she digs her nest, and that the male fertilizes them subsequently; that "they dig a hole or grave and there place their eggs or spawn *after* the milter has done his natural office" (Walton).

The earliest account that I have been able to find, apart from Walton's which is clearly hearsay, is that of Franks (1656). He describes how the female turns on her side and fans the gravel with her tail, while the male assists her by boring into the gravel with his head. Halliday (1824), Young (1849) and Roule (1933) also believed that the male assisted in the preparation of the bed, and even at the present day many fishermen have told me that they thought this to be true.

Shaw (1840), Malloch (1910), Tate Regan (1911) and Hutton (1924) describe the female preparing the bed with her tail, but say the female passes out eggs as she does so: after she has finished making the bed, a male moves up, passes out sperm and fertilizes the eggs. If this were a true description, the wastage of eggs would be very great; one can often see females cutting actively for long periods when there are no males nearer than the resting pools nearby. Females will cut in the absence of males, but to continue cutting they need the stimulus of the male quiver.

Walsh (1863), Calderwood (1931), Belding (1934) and Menzies (1947) have stated that the female makes the bed, and eggs and sperm are passed out simultaneously by the female and male. Menzies suggested (correctly) that a shuddering motion of the male is indicative of the shedding of sperm, but his account of the female's behaviour is incomplete. Belding observed a cloud of sperm being passed out as the male lay alongside the female in the bed; he also noted that it was the *female* which covered up with gravel the bed in which she had passed out eggs. The fact that Salmon hide their spawn ". . . most cunningly and cover it over with gravel and stones and then leave it to the Creator's protection" was already known to Izaak Walton in the 17th century.

Before giving a detailed description of the spawning behaviour in Salmon as seen completely for the first time in the observation-tank at Pont Barcer (see p. 97), some of the terms used need concise definition:

Cutting	The making of the depression or bed by the female (Plate 9, p. 112).
Bed	A single depression made in the gravel by the female.
Feeling	The testing of the gravel by the female with her anal fin and sometimes with her caudal and pelvic fins also.
Crouch	The position adopted by the female in the later stages of feeling the bed.
False Orgasm	An incomplete orgasm in which the female crouches in the

bed accompanied by the male and opens her mouth as if to spawn but does not do so. The male opens his mouth, quivers, and sometimes passes out some sperm before the female relinquishes the crouch position.

Orgasm   The actual and simultaneous extrusion into a bed of a quantity of eggs by the female, and of sperm by the male (Plate 10, p. 113).

Redd   An area of gravel in which eggs are laid (Plate 3b, p. 32).

Spawning Sequence The sequence of events leading up to one orgasm and the covering-up of the eggs.

The observation-tank was constructed on the banks of the River Alwen, a tributary of the Welsh Dee (Plate 8, p. 61). Its primary object was to make it possible to observe, directly and at close range, the behaviour at spawning of male Salmon parr; but there was so much to be learned about the spawning behaviour of the adults, that for the first five years no great strides were made in the parr investigation. The tank was built, with financial assistance from the University of Liverpool, the Dee Fishery Board and the Royal Society, as a continuation of existing Salmon-keeping tanks owned by the Board. Mr. King, Superintendent of the Fishery Board, and I, with the help of the Bailiffs, built the tank, which originally had the following dimensions: length 24 feet, width 5½ feet, depth 4 to 5 feet. In the inshore wall of the tank four armour-plate glass windows were incorporated, the central pair being 6 feet long by 3 feet high and the two end ones 3 feet long by 2½ feet high. The floor of the tank was the river-bed. Plate 8a, p. 61 shows the keeping tanks in the foreground, and, behind them, the observation-tank and the covered observation chamber: Bailiff Stanley Jones is netting a fish out of the keeping tanks for use in the observation-tank.

Before putting the spawning gravel into the tank, I had examined in section several typical spawning grounds in the river and found no common arrangement of the various sizes of gravel; so the task of making a spawning bed in the tank was comparatively easy. Large quantities of gravel were removed from the spawning beds in the river, put into the tank, and raked over; water was allowed to flow over this for some weeks before the start of the experiment. The original spawning-bed in the tank was about 14 feet long with a pool at either end, but we later lengthened it to 18 feet and added another 3-foot window: at the same time the tank itself was extended to 33 feet so as to have an ample resting pool below the enlarged bed. Large stones were put inside the tank away from the windows to produce a natural stream effect and also to force the fish to spawn fairly near the glass. The inflow was controlled by a sluice, and in the bottom wall of the tank other sluices controlled the velocity and depth of the water. The original observation chamber was a lean-to shed, 5½ feet wide and about the same height, running along the whole length of the tank (Plate 8a, p. 61). This shed was eventually enlarged and considerably improved.

In the eight years of the tank's most active service several methods of illuminating it for photographic purposes were tried. The final arrangement was a set of four 1,000-watt tubular tungsten filament lamps, each housed in a reflecting cylindrical paraboloid and so mounted that the set could slide into position over the bed of an actively cutting female. At one stage a dimming device was used, but this was said to cause interference to local radio sets and as the Salmon did not seem to object to bright light its use was limited to one spawning season. The illumination of the tank proved a source of constant worry for the first few years: money was scarce and we were dependent for our electrical supply on an extension of a line which supplied the local cheese-making factory. When the factory was working, which was most of the time, the lights in the tank were seriously affected; at the best, there was a drop of about thirty volts along the line from the factory to the tank.

At the start of the investigation we were not at all certain how the Salmon would react to the light, and how much our presence on the other side of the glass would affect them. In the early days, in order to get enough light to work by in the observation chamber without upsetting the fish, we used candles, candles in darkened jampots, red lights, blue lights, and eventually white lights; at first we used to creep about and talk in whispers. But all these precautions turned out to be quite unnecessary, and it is amusing now to look back on our early antics. We were then very inexperienced, and even now we are still surprised by our success. It is certainly very hard to deter Salmon from spawning when they are in the mood. On the other hand, there is little we can do short of drugging them to encourage them to spawn when they are not ready. Efforts to tempt the fish on to the spawning-bed by artificial spates, by discolouring the water, by altering the colour of the lights, or switching them off, and even by pushing the fish onto the beds with a broom were uniformly unsuccessful.

Salmon on the bed often showed signs of disturbance when a shadow fell on the glass windows from inside the observation chamber, but took no notice of tapping on the glass, moving objects alongside the glass, or even the switching of a 500-watt spotlight directly onto their heads; the switching on of the main top lights also seemed to be unnoticed by the fish, though sometimes the switching of them off upset them for a short time. A major hindrance to observation was the colour of the water during and after floods: at times its turbidity was such that fish only six inches away from the glass were invisible. Many disappointed visitors have suggested filtering the water as a remedy, but the cost would be prohibitive. The site, chosen for compelling financial reasons, had the further disadvantage that when the river rose substantially, tank and chamber were flooded and work had to stop; and for days afterwards the chamber would be damper and colder even than usual. It was several years before the electrical supply was so improved that it would carry the load of an electric fire as well as of the lights.

I have seen over ninety spawnings in the tank, in a total observation-time of over 3,000 hours (Jones and King 1949, 1950). All the spawnings were similar in their general character and the minor variations are attributable to the individuality of the fish taking part and not to the imposition of the restriction of the spawning-tank. After my experience with the tank I can reliably interpret what can be seen in field conditions from a suitable point of vantage: and I am quite satisfied that cutting, courting, spawning and covering-up in the tank are, in all essentials, identical with these processes in natural conditions. In fact I have lately observed spawnings in natural conditions and have been able to confirm the validity of the tank work.

The depth of water on the spawning-gravel in the tank was rarely more than a foot, and Salmon of up to seven pounds weight would spawn readily in six or seven inches of water. The largest fish which spawned there were a male of 30 lbs. and a female of almost 20 lbs. The water moved over the gravel quite rapidly: the velocity which seemed most favourable was between 12 and 18 inches per second at the surface. In order to obtain this flow when the river was low, extra sluices, placed below normal water-level in the lower end-wall of the tank, were opened.

Salmon would not spawn in the tank when the velocity of the water was reduced to two or three inches per second. We found this useful at various times in the later years when observations had to be discontinued for short periods: instead of penning the fish in the pools as we had had to do in the early years of the work, we just partly shut the sluices.

The fish showed a tendency to leap at all times during the spawning seasons, especially at the overfall from the keeping tanks, and occasionally one escaped into the river. Leaping was more frequent and vigorous when the river was high. As the speed and water-level in the tanks were unaltered by changes in the river-level, the fish must have been affected by some change in the quality of water, perhaps its increased turbidity.

Ripe males and females were put into the tank at the beginning of each spawning season, and care was taken to ensure that the females were not "hard" (that is, that the eggs were free in the body-cavity) and that the males were running ripe (that is, that gentle pressure on the flanks resulted in emission of sperm). The fish, which had been handled as little as possible, generally took a week or two to settle down in the tank.

The general pattern of spawning behaviour can be summarised as follows. The males and females spend a considerable time resting in the pools at either end of the spawning bed, though the dominant male will quite frequently interrupt his rest, prod a female with his snout, push against her, or bully any other male. Dominance may be an indication of imminent readiness for spawning: it is certainly not primarily dependent on size, and quite small male fish may appropriate a large female in the presence of much larger males. The next stage is the movement of a female out of the pool and over the gravel. After a series of such exploratory wanderings, the female starts cutting a bed; and as bed-cutting continues, the dominant male quivers with increasing frequency and intensity alongside her. Periodically this female, called for convenience the *tenant,* rests from her activities and either drops back into the pool, or remains stationary in the depression which has resulted from her cutting. The males may fight intermittently, and other females may appear to challenge the tenant female for possession of the bed, though they rarely if ever displace her on that account. As the cutting continues, the tenant tests the result of her activities with her ventral fins, particularly the anal; and when she has made a saucer-like depression about six inches deep, her efforts appear to be directed principally to perfecting the shape of the bed. The end-result is a hole at the bottom of which the current is much reduced: at the bottom of the hole there are two or three large stones between which she can thrust her anal fin as she presses her body into the shape of the bed. When, after hours or even days of fidgety cutting and feeling, the bed is suitable, she assumes the "crouch" position, opens her mouth, and is joined by the male. He also opens his mouth and quivers violently; and the eggs and sperm are extruded almost simultaneously (Plate 10, p. 113). Immediately after the orgasm, the male moves away, generally into the pool below, while the female moves a foot or so upstream from the bed, and by vigorous cutting sends down gravel to fill the depression and cover the eggs. In most spawnings nearly all the eggs are ejected into the crack between the stones at the bottom of the bed, where they are difficult to see and reasonably well sheltered from the shower of gravel which the female afterwards sends down. The "covering-up" is usually continued as the beginning of the next spawning sequence. As many as eight such sequences, each

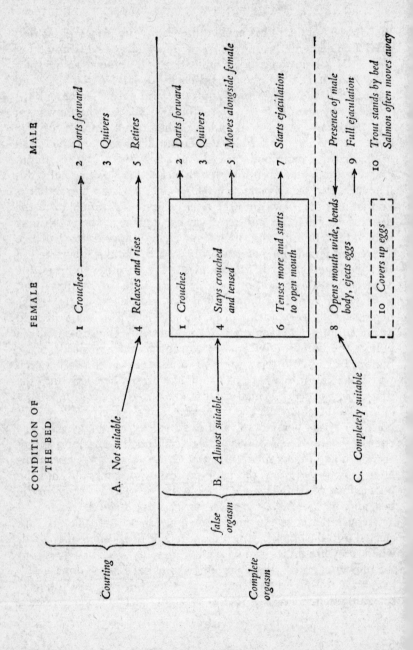

CONDITION OF THE BED   FEMALE   MALE

1   Crouches   2 → Darts forward

3   Quivers

A.   Not suitable   4 → Relaxes and rises   5 → Retires

Courting

1   Crouches   2 → Darts forward

3   Quivers

B.   Almost suitable → 4   Stays crouched and tensed   5 → Moves alongside female

6   Tenses more and starts to open mouth   7 → Starts ejaculation

false orgasm

C.   Completely suitable → 8   Opens mouth wide, bends body, ejects eggs   → Presence of male

9 → Full ejaculation

10   Covers up eggs   10   Trout stands by bed Salmon often moves *away*

Complete orgasm

further upstream than the previous one, may be carried out before the female has deposited all her eggs. An analysis of the orgasm behaviour is given in Fig. 12. p. 102 (Jones and Ball, 1954).

Several aspects of the behaviour-pattern merit further description and discussion. By examination of the slow-motion film I took, it is possible to see that cutting is not a spade-like digging as has sometimes been asserted, and also that cutting is closely related to the feeling movements (Plate 9, p. 112). In cutting, the female turns over on her side and by alternately bending and straightening her body produces a vigorous vertical flapping of her tail; as a result of this the gravel immediately *beneath* her spread caudal fin is dislodged and thrown upwards as the fin moves quickly upward and forward. The larger stones fall quickly, making a parados downstream from the bed, while smaller stones and silt are carried clear away by the current. From my film it is apparent that the female starts a cut from her normal position, that is with head upstream, body on an even keel and almost parallel to the river. She then turns over on her side, usually by first rotating her caudal fin so that it rests almost flat on or near the gravel and then by a lesser rotation of the body, which in this phase is tilted at about 45°. Then the posterior half of her body is bent sharply downwards and her caudal fin rests fanned out on or near the gravel. The bending of the anterior part of her body is less pronounced, so that her head is often only slightly lower than the middle of her body (see Plate 9, p. 112).

From this position follow rapid straightening (the upstroke), and bending (the downstroke), so that the posterior region of her body is thrust vigorously upwards and downwards from and to the gravel. This action of flexing and straightening the body is repeated several times in rapid succession. In the more vigorous cutting movements the anterior part of the body may be more

---

FIG. 12. (*Opposite*) An analysis of the orgasm behaviour of Salmon and trout. Arrows indicate causal relationships, the numbers in brackets indicate chronological sequence of events

bent, so that the fish is an inverted U. Throughout these movements, the pectoral, pelvic and dorsal fins are erected and the mouth is slightly opened. I believe that the vigorous downstroke of the posterior half of the body thrusts the water against the gravel with sufficient force to loosen it. Certainly the upward flexion sucks gravel upwards: individual stones can be seen to follow the tail-fin until they are caught in the current and carried downstream. The complete action of flexing and straightening of the body constitutes one cutting movement, and a complete series of such movements, beginning and ending with the fish in its normal position on an even keel, is called a cut. A weak cut consists of only a few slow and languid cutting movements: a strong cut may consist of as many as a dozen vigorous cutting movements in rapid succession, at the rate of about three or four a second. The female tests or feels the effect of her cutting by means of her anal, caudal and pelvic fins (see below).

Cutting can be conveniently divided into four successive stages:

Stage 1
Random cutting of an exploratory nature; cutting usually weak.

Stage 2
Cutting still exploratory, but applied in a more restricted area; the cuts are long and vigorous and sometimes made at an angle to the current. At this stage the feeling of the bed may take the form of a backing downstream after a cut with pelvic and anal fins touching the disturbed gravel; alternatively, the female circles round to her original position and then moves forwards upstream over the gravel, trailing her pelvic and anal fins over it. At this stage the male is frequently in attendance. He quivers fairly often against or near the female as opportunity offers, but does not follow her backing and circling closely.

Stage 3
The cutting and feeling are now directed to a single limited area until a depression is made with its bottom six inches or more

below the original gravel surface: feeling usually consists in backing down over the bed in such a way that the erect anal fin traverses its floor from its anterior margin to the top of the parados. The male is attentive.

Stage 4

Now the feeling has changed into what is best described as a bouncing movement, in which the female, at first poised a few inches above the deepest portion of the bed, drops slowly and vertically downward with her anal fin erect, until it touches or sometimes slips between the larger stones at the bottom; on contact the downward movement is reversed and she returns to her original position. (At this stage, I think, the main consideration of the female is the accurate positioning of these larger stones. Between these the eggs will be laid and it is these that form the foundation of the protective cover of gravel.) Further cuts are made, but generally not much gravel is displaced, though the larger stones are manoeuvred around with all the appearance of purpose. In so doing, she frequently approximates her wrist (caudal peduncle) rather than her caudal fin to the stones which are to be moved—in this way, it seems,—she can apply to them a gentler and more controlled suction. At this stage the female often presses herself snugly into the bed with her anal fin almost completely hidden between two of the large stones, and her head and the front part of her body raised away from the gravel. This is the "crouch." She may relinquish the crouch after a few moments and proceed to further adjustment of the bed. Or she may remain crouching and, after opening her mouth, pass out a quantity of eggs from her vent. The assumption of the crouch position acts as a signal to the male, who shows signs of excitement and draws closer. As soon as the female begins to open her mouth he slips forward so that his head is alongside of hers, but usually does not lie as deeply in the bed as she. He, too, then opens his mouth and, with fins erect and opercula expanded, quivering violently, he squirts milt into the bottom of the bed. In a normal orgasm the ejection of eggs and milt is simultaneous (Plate 10, p. 113).

Stage 5

Covering-up, which follows immediately on the orgasm, consists of vigorous cutting by the female, directed at a spot a little upstream of the bed in which she has just laid eggs. The stones now lifted fall back over the bed, covering the eggs deeply; this is presumably the primary purpose of the operation. Usually, however, the female treats the depression she has made in covering-up as the beginning of a new bed, and the cycle is repeated with the omission of the first exploratory stages.

If the cutting activity of the female is interrupted at any time during the first three stages, she may sulk and keep away from the bed for hours or even days, but only rarely does a female stop for any length of time when she has reached stage 4.

The depth of the bed varies with the size of the female, and to some extent with the velocity of the water. A large female will make a deeper depression than a small female, and the faster the current generally the deeper the bed. A 12 lb. female may make a depression which at its deepest point may be a foot below the normal gravel level, and may spawn eight times to empty herself, thereby cutting up a length of about sixteen feet of gravel.

The fighting of Salmon seldom results in bloodshed, though the breeding teeth on the elongated jaws are as obviously weapons as are the antlers of a stag. Among many species of animal in which the sex-ratio at maturity is nearly equal and temporary monogamy is the rule, the necessity for actual physical combat is diminished because of the probability that each individual will eventually secure a mate without risking grievous bodily harm or even death. The fighting of such animals is largely replaced by a stylised cycle of challenge and counterthreat, retreat and pursuit, which may look dangerous but is generally quite innocuous. Such is the case with Salmon; and a definite pattern of behaviour is discernible.

Let us begin with a situation in which the dominant male is in close attendance on an actively cutting female. A male intruder slips up from the pool at the bottom of the bed and approaches until his head is perhaps a foot behind that of the dominant male, who now becomes aware of his presence and turns towards him with erect fins. This may be enough to make the intruder drop back; if not, the dominant male turns further and dashes at the intruder with opercula raised and mouth wide open, exposing its livid white interior fringed with teeth. Even to the observer behind his plate-glass window he presents an awe-inspiring spectacle; the intruder invariably turns away downstream and the dominant male follows in pursuit. Usually the intruder turns upstream again towards the female, and the other follows. In this way, both may complete several tight circles before the intruder flees away downstream and the dominant male returns to his watch. This is typical threat-behaviour of a kind often seen when birds defend their territories.

Encounters between females appear less ferocious but have the same stereotyped formality. The occasion is usually when a female who is beginning to cut observes another female who by accident or design has taken up a station just upstream of her. This she appears to resent. She swims forward until her head is ahead of the intruder's. The intruder responds by a similar movement and, by repetition, both move upstream in what we have called "forward parallel progression," a cumbersome but exactly descriptive term. If, as often happens, the intruder edges into the path of the tenant, the latter darts forward and snaps, on which the intruder turns away to swim in a circle and come up again alongside the tenant. Forward parallel progression is then resumed. It is not clear why such an apparently pointless routine should ever stop, but in practice it is broken off after a variable number of repetitions; and one female, almost always the original tenant, drops back and goes on with her cutting where she started. This, too, is seen in the territorial defence behaviour of birds, where the tenant bird nearly always succeeds in driving away an intruder.

It appears that the tenants of a bed are able to distinguish between casual or accidental intrusion and intrusion with malicious intent. For casual intruders on the bed and its vicinity, there are milder forms of reproof. The female in possession, or sometimes the male, moves upstream and then drops down again: and when her tail is a few inches in front of the intruder's nose she flicks it sideways in a way which is easily recognized though difficult to describe. This gesture invariably induces a casual intruder to withdraw downstream. Alternatively, one of the tenants may swim forward and stop obliquely in front of the intruder's nose; the intruder gives way and the two fish move downstream together, maintaining the same relative positions. We have called this manoeuvre *back-pedalling*.

That some intruders' intentions are dishonourable may be inferred from behaviour which, though never yet observed in Salmon, I have seen once (and fortunately photographed) in trout. A male intruder who had previously been driven off succeeded, at the very last moment, in slipping into the bed at the side of the female remote from the tenant male and sharing in the orgasm.

In Salmon, quivering is seen exclusively in males; I have never seen female Salmon quiver though I have seen a female trout do so on three occasions. The quiver is a short sequence of rapid shudders in which the whole body is involved; they seem to start at the head and run along the body. At the same time the dorsal, pectoral and pelvic fins are erected, and sometimes the mouth is opened and the opercular plates slightly distended. When a male is about to quiver alongside a female he generally darts forwards from a position slightly behind her until his head is at about the middle of her body; he may then either move forward along the female's side as he quivers, or may remain stationary. Quivering increases in frequency and intensity up to the orgasm. The male may quiver in the same way against a female that has not been very active in her bed-making: if the female remains inactive despite these attentions of the male, he sometimes attacks her by snapping. The male may sometimes quiver at a distance of three feet from the female, and then there is no

FIG. 13. (*Opposite*) The Male Quiver. Situations in which it occurs and its probable functions

SITUATION	POSSIBLE FACTORS RELEASING QUIVER	PROBABLE FUNCTION OF QUIVER
Against female	Presence of female	Active on or near bed — Courting
		Inactive in the bed — Threat or courting
		Inactive away from bed — Threat or courting
		Intruding in or near bed — Threat
Away from female	Apparently against wall or stone — Possibly presence of solid object	Unknown
	Some distance away from fish or solid object — Unknown	
Against female in orgasm	Crouched tense female	Orgasm
Against male	Presence of male	Threat

MALE QUIVER

preliminary dart forward. Males may quiver against intruding males, or even against males lying away from the bed: unless there is some response to this quivering, the tenant, or dominant male, may launch a biting attack on the other. Finally the male quivers during the orgasm. From the above it is apparent that these quivers may be followed by fighting, may not be followed by fighting, or may end in an orgasm. The quivering behaviour of the Salmon is analysed in Fig. 13, p. 109.

Can we say that the quiver is exclusively an element in courtship (epigamic display)? This was suggested in Jones and King (1949), but not all situations in which the male quivers can readily be recognized as epigamic. Sometimes quivering appears to be used as a threat, though it is not easy to determine even in higher animals where courtship ends and threat-behaviour begins. Is it not possible that the quiver may be used by the male to find out whether another fish is a female, and one which is sexually mature and ready to spawn? If a male quivers against a female and she responds by cutting, the male is informed that she is a female; but if she does not respond by cutting, the male assumes that she is an intruding male and launches an attack upon her. If the male quivers against another male, no female response is given, and again the quivering male may attack. Fabricius (1953) has suggested that the quivering of male char against other males is evidence of homosexuality, but the simpler and more probable explanation is that the male char is simply engaged in checking and correcting his initial assumption about the sex of his partner.

It must be said that it is difficult to fit our observations neatly into the categories of instinctive behaviour created by Lorenz and Tinbergen. Though there are obvious similarities with some of the types of sexual behaviour which they have described and reduced to order, there are obstinate differences. The quiver may be a "sign-stimulus" in their sense: indeed it almost certainly is: but it is something more too. It seems to differ functionally from at least the simpler and more clearly recognized sign-stimuli in the same sort of way that an enquiry differs functionally from a statement or a command. The situation it creates is of a higher order of complexity. If so the analysis by means of models which Tinbergen and van Iersel (1947) and Tinbergen (1948) had applied to the sexual behaviour of the stickleback with such conspicuous success, may prove to be applicable with difficulty, if at all, in the case of the Salmon. We have made some preliminary attempts to introduce a rubber model as the male partner in the spawning sequence of brown trout—a model which, when mechanically driven, simulates the quiver. So far no female has responded unambiguously to it, though males have twice exhibited definite hostility. It is proposed to repeat the experiment with an improved version. In contending that the sexual behaviour of Salmon is more complex and less easily categorized than that of the stickleback, I do not claim uniqueness for many of its interesting features. Analogies will immediately occur to students of the behaviour of birds and mammals, and readers less familiar with what is now a very large subject may like to consult the more general chapters of Tinbergen's book *The Study of Instinct* (1951), and Tinbergen (1952).

From this account it is clear that the spawning of Salmon is a close-knit co-operative enterprise with a clear-cut division of labour. It cannot be completed unless the water is right, the gravel is right, and at least one Salmon of each sex is present and in the right physiological condition. Though I cannot specify exactly in what rightness consists, my tank observations give a fairly good idea of which factors are important and which are not. It is clear, for example, that the depth of water is unimportant within quite wide limits, whereas the current velocity is of great importance, possibly because the making of an efficient bed depends on the winnowing effect of the current in carrying off smaller particles and silt. Light is of relatively little importance: spawning continues when the water is almost opaque with suspended matter and certainly in the tank it continues throughout the hours of darkness. On the other hand, in the tank, spawning has only proceeded to completion when the water temperature has been between 2°C and 6°C, though it has been observed in the river at a temperature as high as 10°C.

Below 1°C cutting is languid, beds are not finished and the orgasm does not take place.

The tank experiments do throw a little light on what makes gravel right for spawning purposes. Since the redd was made by taking gravel from natural redds and throwing it down anyhow, it is obvious that there are no special and necessary properties associated with deposition by natural means. The gravel consists largely of irregularly shaped stones varying between 7 inches and a quarter of an inch in their largest dimension, with a very small proportion of sand and silt. Such a mixture cannot be compacted, and the spaces between the stones allow water to flow freely, see Chap. 9. The velocity is of course much less than in the stream above, but is adequate to supply eggs and alevins with all the oxygen they need. Cutting is never observed on the concrete floor of the keeping-tank and it is reasonable to suppose that the female is responding to the gravel's surface-texture perceived through contact with the sensitive anal fin. Fabricius, however, has seen trout trying to cut on a plate-glass sheet overlying gravel; so it appears that visual recognition alone is sometimes enough.

Even when all physical requirements are satisfied, the physiological and psychological state of the participants must be right. In the absence of a female the male, of course, gets nowhere. In the absence of an adult male the female does not proceed further than the early exploratory cuts. (As will be seen in the next chapter, the presence of a ripe male parr is not enough, though he is perfectly able to fertilize her eggs if she could be persuaded to lay them). It is this early cutting which appears to excite the sexual interest of the male, though only if he too is ripe. From this point onwards it appears that active cutting by the female and repeated quivering by the male are both necessary if the act is to be completed. Laggardly cutting is reciprocated at first by

Plate 9 (*opposite*)

A female salmon cutting a bed. Enlarged by Mr. Lee from the author's cine-film. Note the curvature of the body. This sequence represents one series of cuts. (*J. W. Jones*)

more intense quivering. If this is ineffective the male behaviour may be transformed to overt hostility or, if an alternative partner is available, even desertion. On the other hand, if the male does not quiver or is removed, the female makes little further progress with her bed.

When the bed is nearly complete the female may crouch several times between the cuts which put the final touches to it. At each crouch the male shows excitement and when he finally joins the female, eggs and sperm are normally shed together. The presence of the male is a necessary but not a sufficient condition for the shedding of eggs. The female never deposits the eggs unless the male is there and ready to fertilize them. But he may join her and even shed sperm when no eggs are forthcoming. This is the false orgasm. The human observer cannot distinguish with certainty the crouch which is the last stage of feeling, from the crouch which indicates immediate readiness for the orgasm: and it appears as if the male Salmon cannot do so either. Perhaps there is no difference: an occasional false orgasm with its consequent waste of milt may be an economical price to pay for ensuring that the eggs are covered with milt at the instant they are laid.

It has been emphasized already that a normal spawning is very economical. The wastage of eggs is small and their percentage fertilization is high. Of the ninety-odd spawnings

---

Plate 10 (opposite) Spawning of the brown trout.
Above.   A quiver. Male 'courting' female. (*W. Lee*)

Centre.   Brown trout during the orgasm adopt the same positions as do salmon. This photograph taken in my trout spawning tank at Liverpool by Mr. Lee, shows clearly how the female fish pushes her body well down into the bed as she lays her eggs, and the male lies alongside her as he passes out sperm. The male in this photograph has just extruded his sperm which can be seen as a faint white cloud and has closed his mouth. The female still has her mouth open and is passing out eggs, one or two of which can be seen clearly in the picture.

Below.   Female just spawned disturbs some of her own eggs. Note sperm. Male stands by. (*W. Lee*)

observed in the tank, there was only one case in which a substantial proportion of the eggs failed to stay in the bed and were carried away by the current. In this case the female was clearly sick, for she died soon after and the post-mortem disclosed internal haemorrhage; it is reasonable to suppose that she was incapable of making a proper bed. In normal spawnings the number of eggs seen to escape is rarely as many as twenty and may often be none at all out of the total of several hundred laid.

TABLE 2

Percentage fertilisation of Eggs in the Salmon Observation-Tank

Bed No.	Total eggs	No. dead eggs	Per cent dead eggs
1 (two females)	185 (+273 in February)	5 (+15 not yet eyed in Feb.)	2·7 (5·4)
2	1,065	23	2·1
3	1,029	5	0·5
4	712	21	2·9
5	1,153	4	0·3
6 and 7	1,183	5	0·4
8	383	5	1·3
Total	5,983	83	1·4

An estimate of the percentage of successful fertilization is attended with some difficulty because, within thirty-six hours of fertilization, the eggs become extremely sensitive to disturbance, and remain so for many weeks until development is almost complete. When they can safely be moved and handled again, they are called *eyed ova* because the eyes can be seen as black dots through the membrane of each egg. Dead or unfertilized eggs can then be recognized by the absence of eyes. They are usually also no longer translucent but dead white, owing to protein precipitation. In March 1947, we made counts of the eggs in eight beds made by one female in the previous November. The results are summarised in Table 2. Unfortunately the first bed was so close to one made by another female that the eggs could not be separated. Probably too, some eggs were lost from this bed when it was opened in February to see how far development had gone. The total of eggs recovered from nine spawning acts was therefore 5,983, of which only 83 were dead (less than 2 per cent). The 1,024 eyed ova from Bed 3 were transferred to the hatchery and, despite the necessary handling, 98·5 per cent of them hatched.

In the following year 10,074 eyed ova and 252 (ca. 2·5 per cent) dead eggs were collected from 12 beds (average per bed 874 living, 21 dead). All the eyed ova were transferred to the hatchery and only 8 failed to hatch. The slightly higher mortality (2½ per cent) in this year is attributable to a slightly greater degree of overcutting (interference with a completed bed by subsequent cutting). Plate 3b, p. 32, shows a salmon redd opened to expose a few of the eggs.

Cutting is as characteristic an activity of the ripe female Salmon as quivering is of the male. No female has been seen to quiver and it is of interest that the only male ever seen to cut had previously been castrated for a purpose which will be made clear in the next chapter. This male had also been treated with a male hormone (testosterone propionate in pellets) in the hope that he would continue to behave as a male in spite of castration; but the method of administering testosterone in this case was subsequently shown to be ineffective, (the pellets were not absorbed, they were later removed from the fish unchanged), and there is little doubt his cutting was solely due to castration. The male began to cut about three weeks after the operation. When I saw it (at about seven o'clock in the morning after a long night watch) I was so astonished that I doubted my eyes and rushed away to fetch Bailiff Stanley Jones as a witness. It was unfortunately not possible to continue a watch on the behaviour of this male, but even this brief observation is enough to suggest that cutting is the expression of an instinctive motor pattern present in both sexes but normally suppressed in the male by his testicular hormones.

CHAPTER 7

THE SALMON IN THE RIVER—II

The Spawning of the Male Parr

THE account of spawning given in the preceding chapter was intentionally left incomplete. The part played by the male Salmon parr merits a chapter to itself.

It has long been known that some male Salmon parr attain sexual maturity before they leave the river, but such fish have until recently been regarded as exceptional and not as playing a normal or functional part in the life-history of the Salmon.

As long ago as 1837, Shaw, a Scots water-bailiff whose pioneer work on artificial fertilization has been mentioned in Chapter 2, p. 19, carried out experiments with the sperm of a ripe male Salmon parr. He took a female Salmon weighing 4 lb. and a male Salmon parr weighing about ½ oz. from the spawning-bed in a river. Some of the eggs obtained from the female Salmon were fertilized with the parr's sperm; the eggs were then put in a stream where the young, as he believed, hatched out as normal alevins. Unfortunately he had not on this occasion kept his eggs segregated, nor did he run a control experiment. Later he took another female (11 lb.) and four male parr from the same spawning bed and impregnated four different lots of her eggs, one lot by the sperm of each parr. The parr used in the experiment were kept in a pond, and became smolts in the following May. The four batches of fertilized eggs were hatched in a stream to which no Salmon had access, and became mature in eighteen months. Three ripe parr from each of these batches were used to fertilize eggs from an adult female Salmon, and again these matured.

These experiments seem conclusive of the adequacy of parr sperm to fertilize eggs without producing any abnormality, for two consecutive generations, but in 1887, Day still believed "that male parrs and smolts may afford milt competent to fertilize ova, but when from fish from the second season, or up to thirty-two months old, it is (always?) of insufficient strength for strong and vigorous fry to be raised . . ."

Young female Salmon rarely, if ever, become sexually mature in the river. Shaw remarked that, very exceptionally, large female parr with well-developed eggs had been found, and there are other isolated reports, but I am not at all certain that some of them do not refer to sea-trout. Tate Regan reported on a ripe female parr from the River Teme (1938); as mentioned previously (p. 17) Teme parr and smolts appear to be exceptionally large and need further investigation.

Unfortunately Shaw was primarily concerned to show that parr were in fact young Salmon. He did not attempt to prove that the sexual maturity of the males was common and normal in the life-history of the fish. Day and his contemporaries were mainly interested in showing that young Salmon in enclosed waters could develop gonads. It was not till 1911 that Dahl reported the high percentages of ripe males amongst the parr and smolts from the rivers of Norway and Finland, and even he did not believe that these fish would spawn until they had been down to the sea and had returned to the river the following year. Carr (1913) believed that the ripe male parr which she had found in the Wye would spawn before going to sea. Pentelow *et al.* (1933) showed that male smolts in the Tees fell clearly into two groups, one with small immature testes and one with large testes, which migrated earlier than the first group. I believe that histological examination would have shown that the testes of the second group were in fact spent (see below for description of a spent testis). I, myself, have examined a sample of parr from spawning grounds of the River Oloron in France, and all of these proved to be ripe or spent males.

The presence on spawning beds of male parr which are ready to shed their milt or have already shed it is therefore either con-

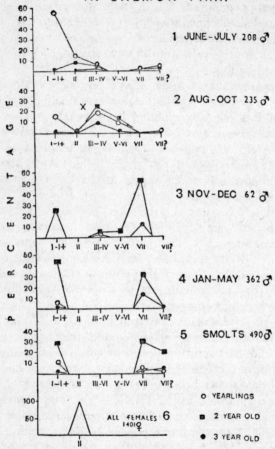

FIG. 14. Percentage frequency of gonad phases in yearling, two year-old, and three year-old male Salmon parr and smolts. 1. Beginning of the sexual cycle. 2. End of period of gonad development. 3. The spawning period. 4. The post-spawning period. 5. The migratory period (smolts).* 6. Females only—gonads immature at all times.

* *Erratum:* IV and VI should be transposed.

firmed or strongly indicated all over the Atlantic seaboard from France to Finland. There are also records of ripe male Salmon parr from at least one North American river.

Our investigation of this phenomenon began in 1937 when a sample of parr received from the Dee in October was examined and nearly all were found to be sexually mature males. During the next two years about three thousand parr and smolts from twenty British rivers were examined. About half of these fish were males, and of these about 75 per cent were ripe (sexually mature), spending (in the process of spawning), or spent (finished spawning). Of the smolts examined, 60 per cent of the males were definitely spent. Not one of the 1,500 females examined were maturing, mature or spent (Orton, Jones and King, 1938, Jones and Orton, 1940).

In parr which are about to mature, the testis shows a seasonal developmental cycle: it starts to ripen or develop in June to July, and by August some may be fully mature but not running ripe. Ripe fish were taken up to December or January; from then on until the smolt migration a large proportion were partly or wholly empty. Most of the maturing, mature, or spent fish were in the second year of their life, but I found some spent yearling smolts in the Hampshire Avon.

Figure 14 (p. 118) shows the percentage frequency of the gonad phases in relation to age and time of year; from this figure the sexual cycle can easily be followed.

I was able to show that in the sexual cycle of parr, spermatogenesis is normal (Jones, 1940). In their least developed state, the testes are a pair of long thread-like bodies, slightly translucent, but generally of an even grey colour, situated dorsal to the gut and slightly below and to one side of the air-bladder. Testes in this immature state are found in some male parr throughout the year, and their presence in two-year-old fish at the beginning of the spawning season is an indication that such fish would not have become mature in that season. It is, however, possible that, if these fish had remained in the river for a third year, they might have ripened the following spawning season.

The first signs of maturation can be seen with the naked eye;

the testes widen slightly at the front end and often become slightly rosy in colour, the posterior end remaining thread-like. As their development proceeds, they increase in size, and their colour changes from rosy to light grey, then to greasy white, and finally to milky white. The widening starts at the anterior end, and spreads back to extend nearly the length of the body-cavity. From this stage (II) the testes enlarge to fill up almost all the body cavity; at their posterior ends wide ducts unite just before entering the genital papilla. A diagrammatic representation of the sequence is given in Figure 15, p. 121.

After the spawning season, the testes show signs of collapse; they are milky white in patches only and their colour becomes mainly peachy and eventually fawny; in the smolts only a few white patches of relict sperm are to be found, generally in the ducts: eventually all the white patches disappear and the testes become a uniform fawn.

All the colour-changes in the testes can be related to the internal changes which are taking place during the spermatogenesis. As the testes enlarge anteriorly, spermatogonia are found, and the presence of spermatids and sperm is correlated with the appearance of the white colour.

It is not possible by external examination to distinguish a mature male Salmon parr from a female or immature male until it is "running-ripe". There are no secondary sexual characteristics, no kype is developed and no colour-changes occur. But the habits of the mature male parr are different from those of the females and immature males. As I said in Chapter 6, they migrate upstream just before and during the spawning season, and are to be found in large numbers on the spawning grounds in November and December.

After starting our investigations, we repeated under controlled conditions Shaw's experiment with parr sperm. In November, 1937, a 17 lb. female Salmon was stripped into a clean basin. The eggs were then mixed thoroughly by hand and divided into two equal batches, one being fertilized by parr sperm and the other by that of an adult of about 10 lb. weight. The eggs so fertilized were transported to Chirk Fish Hatchery and kept

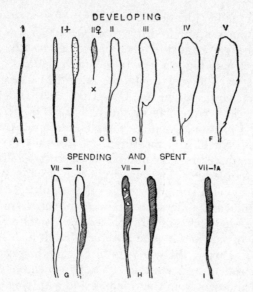

FIG. 15. Stages in the development and spending of the testes of ripe male salmon parr.

A. Stage I, Gonadial tube present about 1 mm. wide.

B. Stage 1+, Slight widening at anterior end of gonad.

C. Stage, II, Gonad about 5 mm. wide.

D. Stage III, Gonad filling about half the abdominal cavity.

E. Stage IV, Gonad filling rather more than half the b ᴧy cavity.

F. Stage V, Gonad full grown filling all the available space in the body cavity.

G. Stage VII–II, Collapsed testes in which some relict sperms may be present, shown unshaded in diagram.

H. Stage VII–1+, Very little sperm left, mostly in duct, testes still collapsing.

I. Stage VII–IA, No sperm present, testes completely spent.

The figure does not show developmental stages 0 and VI, nor the intermediate stages of spending. No gonad is visible to the naked eye at Stage 0. The Stage VI gonad is of the same size as that in Stage V, but gonadial elements ooze to the exterior with only slight pressure on the flanks of the fish. At Stages VII–IV and Stage VII–III, the emptying gonads are of the same size respectively as the developing gonads in Stages IV and III.

separate but under identical conditions. After a year, when a random sample of a hundred fry from each batch was measured, there was no significant difference in average length. Owing to the war I was not able to measure these fish again.

After the war the experiment was repeated. The eggs in this instance were transported to Calverton Fish Hatchery near Nottingham, and were left in the able care of Mr. O'Brien. Periodically I measured random samples, and after two years all the fish were caught and measured. 784 of the parr's progeny had survived, three times the number of surviving adult's progeny, though this difference may be irrelevant to the question of whether parr sperm is more vigorous than adult sperm.* There was no significant difference in average length or condition between the two batches of fish. So, up to the smolt stage at least, the progeny of parr are as good as those of adult males (Jones and King, 1950). During the war Alm in Sweden had carried out a similar experiment and come to the same conclusion (1943).

A problem arises from the ripening and emptying of the male parr gonads. It will be remembered that the scales of adult Salmon are eroded during their stay in the river and that the scars so produced are called spawning-marks. Is such a scar produced on the scales of male parr? Southern (1933) after examining the scales of male parr from the Shannon thought that well-developed spawning-marks were to be seen on these scales. He concluded that these marks were the result of scale-erosion and noted that the amount of erosion differed appreciably on scales from the same fish; only a trace of a spawning-mark was apparent on some scales. In 1940, Frost and Went failed to find evidence of any erosion on the scales of young Salmon from the Liffey. At the same time they examined fresh samples of scales from the mature parr studied by Southern but were unable to find any spawning-marks; nor did Carr (1913) find any on the scales of ripe parr from the Wye.

In 1937 I started examining large samples of Dee parr and smolt scales for evidence of spawning, either in the form of a

---

* This difference in survival may be due to the genetic differences between the individual parr and the individual adult, not to the difference in age and size.

mark, or of some difference in growth-ring pattern. I thought it possible that the ripening of the testes might be reflected in retarded growth and a consequent change in the rate and type of growth-ring formation. For the purpose of this investigation the scales were separated into two groups:

a. from male parr in which the testes were in a state of advanced maturity, mature, or spent;
b. immature males and females.

The average number of growth-rings on about thirty scales from each fish was counted and compared—a tedious and fruitless occupation. No spawning-mark was seen on any scale, and there was no indication from these counts that growth-ring formation or scale-development was in any way different in the spawning and non-spawning fish. This result is perhaps not very surprising, for ripening parr continue to feed voraciously even at spawning time when the water-temperature is low. It may be assumed that there is not the same necessity to draw on the tissues of the body as there is in adult Salmon, whose fast is absolute; there is the further consideration that they are physiologically adapted to fresh water and in this respect resemble brown trout, on which scale-erosion at spawning is very slight, while on sea-trout it is considerable.

Meanwhile the Salmon observation-tank had been built, primarily for the purpose of investigating the sexual behaviour of the male Salmon parr. But during the first few years of the experiment, though we watched many adult spawnings, and saw interesting and previously unsuspected aspects of the behaviour of both adults and parr, we could not prove that parr sperm fertilized any eggs in a natural spawning.

As early as 1947, it was clear from our tank-observations that male parr were very interested in any adult female which was cutting. Whenever she moved on to the bed, one or two male parr would follow, and would stay with her despite the perpetual bombardment of stones thrown about by her cutting activity. One exceptionally daring parr was christened "Dick Barton". When several parr were in attendance one always assumed dominance over the others, choosing his own station and chivying any other parr which got in his way. The parr in attendance on the female were not passively tolerated by the adult fish: if they made themselves conspicuous, either adult would threaten them by open-mouthed lunges or darts, though they were never caught or bitten. Their evasive tactics were usually a rapid dart forward out of the bed, followed by a quick turn around and another dart backwards to the comparatively safe position under the belly of the adults, where they could not be seen. At other times they would freeze motionless when attacked, pressing themselves into the gravel; this posture would be held for minutes at a time until the adult moved away.

The favourite position of the male parr was just under and behind the vent of the female. Sometimes when the female left her partly-made bed, the dominant parr would remain on guard and would drive away intruding parr and small trout. Once, when an intruding parr, of approximately the same size as the dominant parr, ventured into the bed, the dominant parr darted at him with mouth open, grasped him just behind the head and apparently threw him out of the bed. In the early stages of bed-preparation, the parr stayed in the bottom of the bed or lay on the mound of gravel downstream from the bed; they appeared to be conscious of every movement made by the female. Should the female move upstream out of the bed, the parr invariably accompanied her; and there have been times when I thought that a parr was trying to drive her back into the bed by the "tail-flicking" behaviour described for adults in Chapter 6, p. 92. During the last stages of cutting the parr invariably reacted to the crouch of the female by darting to a position deep in the bed and close to her vent. There were occasions when the parr disappeared completely between the large stones at the bottom of the bed—the exact place destined for the eggs to be deposited. At this stage it was also apparent that the sexual drive in the parr over-rode any territorial behaviour, since two, three, or more parr might congregate in the bottom of the bed as the female crouched. Parr are seen to quiver, but only when the female is crouching or lying in the bed. The parr's quiver appears identical with that of the adult and is usually performed in close proximity to the vent of the female; sometimes, indeed, the protruding vent of the adult female is touched by a quivering parr; unlike adult males the parr never gape when quivering, except at the orgasm (see below).

The sum of all our observations at this stage left us firmly convinced, though still unable to prove, that the parr were effective partners in the spawning act. All the circumstantial evidence appeared to favour a genuine sexual precocity, but the possibility remained that it was only practice—a form of play which foreshadowed adult sexual activity, as the play of kittens foreshadows adult hunting.

We naturally tried the obvious experiment of leaving a ripe adult female in the tank with mature parr only (1946); but after a very brief spell of weak cutting the female discontinued her activities. It was suspected that this female might have been physically not able to spawn; so at a later date on two occasions a female was firstly allowed to spawn once with an adult male to show that she was capable of spawning; then the adult male was removed and the female left in the tank with only the mature parr. She did not spawn with the parr; but when the adult male was returned to the tank after an interval, she continued spawning with him.

Thus to obtain conclusive evidence that the parr were adequate sires in a natural spawning it was clearly necessary that a male adult should be present at the spawning, and that he should behave normally in every way except for the actual emission of milt into the bed. Many attempts in 1949 to make an adequate contraceptive device which could be applied externally proved unsuccessful. If the devices were loose they were rubbed off at once, and if they were tight they seemed to constitute a psychological impediment to normal behaviour. In following years this method was abandoned in favour of an operative procedure; a ripe adult male was anaesthetized with 0·5 per cent urethane in river water and sterilized by ligating the testicular ducts. For this a two-inch incision was made in the abdominal wall just in front of the vent, and was subsequently closed with sutures or operating clips. Care was needed to avoid puncturing the thin wall of the testis, as otherwise milt might have escaped into the body-cavity and so to the exterior through the incision, when the fish was in the act of spawning. After a successful operation the sterilized male recovered in about twenty minutes and courted the female with the usual ardour; his behaviour appeared normal in every way except that no milt was emitted at the orgasm. After each experiment the sterilized fish were removed from the spawning tank and pressure exerted on their flanks to see if any sperm could be forced out. In no instance was it possible to do this; the ligatures held and so did the unpunctured testes. None of the males died as a result of this operation.

An alternative method was castration by complete removal of the testes. I first tried to dissect out the testes, but the operation proved lengthy and arduous, and an incision had to be made along the entire length of the abdomen and was consequently difficult to close. I eventually used a technique whereby only a small incision was made in the middle line. I then inserted two fingers through the incision and pulled the testes out with a gentle but firm pull; there was little, if any, loss of blood and the testes came out intact. Some of the castrates were injected with testosterone propionate (Organon) and others had 100 mg. pellets of it planted intramuscularly in their backs. The object of this was to counter-balance the lack of male hormone consequent on castration, and ensure the continuance of normal male behaviour. The pellets, however, were ineffective, and when subsequently removed, showed no signs of absorption. Injection is unsatisfactory in fish because the wound made by the needle does not close as soon as the needle is withdrawn, as it does in most higher vertebrates, and a great though indeterminate part of any dose flows out again and is wasted.

Recovery after this operation, which is technically much easier than ligation of the ducts, appears to be complete: but none of the Salmon resumed courtship activity, and in one case at least, as mentioned in the last chapter, there was a reversal of sexual behaviour and the castrated male began to cut as if he were a female. I therefore relied entirely on sterilized males and soon obtained satisfactory results. I have now seen fourteen spawning acts in which the only milt has been provided by the parr. Twice a parr was actually seen to emit sperm at the instant when the eggs were deposited, though usually the parr are so deep in the bed that all that can be seen is the cloud of milt drifting up rather later. The parr gape and quiver at the orgasm as do the adult males, but unlike them they stay in the bed afterwards until displaced by the gravel with which the female covers up (Jones and King, 1952).

Before these parr spawnings had been observed, many people assured me that the parr were interested, not in spawning, but solely in the opportunity to eat the eggs. There is no doubt that male Salmon parr do eat eggs; the stomach contents of parr from the spawning tank were examined each year, and many were full of Salmon eggs. But I never saw a parr take any eggs from the bed of the female with whom he had just spawned. Often, as she moved out of the bed after an orgasm, the spawning parr could be seen at the bottom of the bed lying on the few eggs exposed, but they never took them. Parr have, however, been seen later to eat any stray eggs which escaped out of the nest during spawning: and they are certainly quick to snap up any eggs which are displaced by overcutting.

Later examination of the gonads of the parr used in the various experiments have shown that in every instance the parr were spent. On the other hand, the parr kept in the stock-tank were still running-ripe.

In 1951, after seven parr spawnings (in the presence of a sterilized male adult) the female was prevented from covering her eggs, which were collected and transferred in separate batches in the hatchery. There was thus no danger of mistaking these eggs for any others which might have been in the gravel in the spawning-tank. By the following March, 2,436 of the 2,504 eggs so collected were eyed, giving a fertilization figure of 97·7 per cent. These spawnings were successfully filmed.

Why is it necessary for the parr to supplement the function of the adult male? At first sight, it appears that nature is unduly wasteful, but after observing over ninety spawnings I am of the opinion that the contribution of the ripe male parr at spawning is, like other features of the spawning act, a safety precaution of considerable importance. It will be remembered that Salmon spawn in rapidly moving water; that at the bottom of the bed the water-current, though much reduced, is not zero; that though the female at orgasm is crouching hard down on to the bottom of the bed, the male may pass out his sperm when his vent is three or four inches from the bottom; and, finally, that the milt becomes ineffective very quickly on dilution with river-water. If by any chance the female has made a poor bed, or if the male in his excitement misjudges his position in the bed, it is conceivable that his sperm, however forcibly ejaculated, may not get down to the eggs. But as the parr are always at the bottom of the bed, in most instances lower than the vent of the female, their sperm will almost certainly have a good chance of reaching the eggs. The parr represent a form of biological insurance (see also Chapter 8, p. 131).

It will not be an easy task to find out what proportion of eggs are naturally fertilized by Salmon parr, though the availability of radioactive tracer elements makes it theoretically possible. For this purpose it would be necessary to use as a tracer element a constituent of a substance (possibly phosphorus) which would in the first place be assimilable by the fish, in the second place would contribute preferentially to the synthesis of the nucleoproteins of which the sperm-head is chiefly composed, and in the third place would retain its radioactivity for the necessary period. If these conditions can be satisfied, it should then not be too difficult to find out what proportion of the eggs have been fertilized by the parr sperm in the rather favourable conditions of the observation-tank. If, however, I am right in thinking of the parr contribution as a form of insurance, it may well prove that it only plays an important role in adverse conditions such as unusually fast currents, unmanageable gravel, etc. As seventy-five per cent of male parr become sexually mature it may be that this state of affairs is a stable feature of the species, a balanced dimorphism. If so, the difference between the sexually mature male parr and the non-maturing male parr will be controlled by a pair of allelomorphs (alternative forms of the genes which carry the

Plate 11. Gaur Fish Pass, in the Tummel-Garry scheme. (*W. Ralston Ltd.*)

a

b

characters in the eggs and sperm), and the proportion of the two types of male will remain relatively constant and will be determined by natural selection (Huxley, 1955, Ford, 1945). Alternatively, it is possible that we are witnessing an evolutionary change —a step perhaps towards the abandonment of the migratory habit. Can it also be assumed that all the progeny of a mature parr will spawn as parr? Will the smolt progeny of a spawning in which a parr took no part migrate to the sea without spawning?

Plate 12 (opposite)

a. A male salmon being stripped; note the white streams of milt or sperm which will be mixed by hand with the eggs. Generally many more eggs are present in the basin. (_Russell Westwood "Illustrated"_)

b. Two male salmon badly attacked by fungus. One showing a well developed kype. (_P. D. H. Malloch_)

CHAPTER 8

THE RETURN TO THE SEA

BY the end of the spawning season most of the Salmon are in a sorry state, very different from those which "being in season at their first taking out of the water . . . their bodies adorned with such red spots, as give them such an addition of natural beauty, as I think was never given to any woman by the artificial paint or patches, in which they so pride themselves in this age." (Walton).

At this stage of their life, both males and females are called kelts. Many show the wear and tear of their long fast and spawning activities; some suffer from "salmon disease", an infection by *Bacillus salmonis pestis*, which enters the flesh through a cut or abrasion, and from this point attacks and destroys adjacent tissue. The external indications of this disease are white patches of *Saprolegnia ferox*, a fungus which preferentially grows on the flesh killed by the bacilli (Patterson, 1903: see Plate 12b, p. 129. "Salmon disease" must not be confused with furunculosis, a more serious and now fortunately much less common bacterial disease of salmon (see Appendix III, p. 158); many kelts escape it. Fish which have not been long in the river before spawning may be caught as "well-mended kelts" early in the following fishing season; they are often, quite understandably, mistaken for clean fish.

When the female Salmon has finished spawning, she soon drops back to the nearby resting pool, where she may stay a while before continuing her journey to the sea. The male, on the other hand, tends to stay on the beds, fighting, and possibly looking for further mates. I am sure that an adult male often spawns with more than one hen; and, even when the testes are apparently emptied, male fish seem still to have an urge to spawn, which keeps them on the spawning beds. It is possible that herein lies an additional explanation of the precociousness of parr. If an empty or nearly empty male induced a female to pass out eggs which he was incompetent to fertilize, the active sperm would be provided by the omnipresent parr. This, as we have seen, happens in the tank as a result of human intervention, and there is no reason to suppose it does not happen naturally. As a result of the persistence of sexual activity in the males, the proportion of males to females on the redd increases as the spawning season advances. Though I have never seen them, Menzies (1931) has reported spawning beds with an entirely male population.

When the much exhausted Salmon start their arduous journey back to the sea, which, as will be seen later, many will never reach, they usually drop downstream tail first. They are still positively rheotactic, and, though they are too much weakened to make headway against the current or even to keep station, fast-moving water may stimulate them to sudden short-lived bursts of activity. I have not seen many kelts moving downstream, but all that I saw (when I was keeping watch at the old hydro-electric station grid at Chester) came downstream tail first. The fish which reach the sea quickly begin to recover from the ill effects of their spawning; they start feeding again, and some eventually return to spawn once more. However, not many males survive to make a second journey. Hutton (1922), who has dealt at some length with the mortality of Wye fish after spawning, examined scales of 11,455 Wye Salmon of both sexes taken between 1908 and 1920. He found that only 883 (7.7 per cent) were spawning a second time, and of these, less than 10 per cent were males. In the Wye, therefore, only 0.7 per cent of the males return to spawn a second time.

Hutton, in company with many others, emphasizes that small Salmon are not necessarily young Salmon; a proportion of the older fish are those which have spawned once or even twice and which, though they regain condition completely in the sea, never make as much growth as maiden fish of the same age. A six-year-old maiden Salmon, having spent four years in the sea, may weigh forty pounds at the start of its first spawning run. But a fish of almost the same age which has already spawned at three sea-years, may weigh only twenty-five pounds when entering the river on its second spawning run—little more, in fact, than on its first.

The *absence-periods* or lengths of time the Salmon spends in the sea between spawnings are for convenience classified in three groups:

1. Short period.   a few months' duration: *i.e.* when kelt goes down in spring and comes up the following autumn to spawn again.
2. Long period.   about a year: i.e. a whole summer and winter is spent in the sea.
3. Very long period.   a stay in the sea of about eighteen months.

The absence-period, which can be roughly estimated from the scales of returning fish may be characteristically different in different rivers. In the Wye most of the fish stay in the sea about a year before returning to spawn a second time (Hutton, 1937). In 1908, 12 per cent returned after a short absence-period, 86 per cent after a long absence-period, and only 3 per cent after a very long absence-period. Of 873 marked fish, 74 returned to spawn a third time.

It is interesting to note that the absence-period on the second return to the sea is not necessarily the same as on the first. In the Welsh Dee I found the proportion of long-absence to short-absence fish to be 3:1; all the short-absence fish were small summer fish (2+). This finding is consistent with the belief that the longer a fish spends fasting in the river, the longer it needs to recuperate in the sea afterwards, but there are doubtless many exceptions to so simple a rule. In Eire, Went (1947) found in 1944 that the proportion of previous spawners varied from 0·6 per cent in the River Liffey to 9·5 per cent in the River Erne, the average being 4·3 per cent, and in the following year it varied from 0·6 per cent in the River Boyne to 15·4 per cent in the River Erne. Went gives a table of statistics for nineteen Irish rivers, and says that "Previous spawners are roughly equivalent in Eire to two-thirds of the total catch by rod and line, and therefore anything we can do to preserve the kelts is a small but positive contribution to the stocks of Salmon in our rivers." It was noticeable in Eire, as in the Welsh Dee, that summer fish returned after a short absence in the sea, whereas spring fish adopted the long-absence habit; and, of course, it was these latter fish that put on most weight in the sea.

Menzies (1931) gives a striking example of the survival of spawned Salmon in a small river. He found that in a small west-coast river, the Add, 34 per cent of the incoming population had already spawned at least once. This, as far as he knew then, was unusual and did not occur in any other small river which had been investigated. He thought that it might have some relationship to the small size of the river and the absence of netting. However, in the Grimersta, a small river in Lewis, which has not been netted for many years, the percentage of previous spawners was only about five; this and other negative results indicate that the size of the river and the presence or absence of nets have little to do with the survival of the kelts.

Kelts do not make good eating. Patton showed that during and after spawning time the food-value of the fish is greatly reduced. But after a few months in the sea, these fish on their return to the river have a body-muscle and abdominal-wall muscle fat-content at least as high as, in some cases higher than, that of virgin fish. Kelts are therefore worth preserving; once they are safely back in the sea they soon become worthwhile Salmon. Hutton and Went give several instances. One 8 lb. kelt returned in fifteen months as a 28 lb. fish; out of a large number of tagged kelts with an average weight of 5·4 lb., those recaptured averaged 11 lb.

The proportion of kelts that survive for a third spawning is comparatively small. In Eire, Went found that nearly 97 per cent of mended kelts were returning for a second spawning, 3 per cent for a third spawning, and an infinitesimal number (less than one-tenth of one per cent) for a fourth spawning. In the Wye, 8·4 per cent of all fish returned twice, 0·7 per cent three times, and 0·02 per cent four times. Nall has described the scales of Salmon caught in Loch Maree, Scotland, which had spawned four times. It was thirteen years old and is probably the oldest recorded Scottish Salmon; it had always returned to the river as a spring fish. Menzies describes the scales of a Canadian Salmon which had spawned four times; it had been a two-year-old smolt, had spent three years in the sea before its first spawning, and, like the Maree fish, had been five years old at its first spawning; but the latter had spent three years in the river and spawned for the first time as a two-sea-year-old fish (small spring fish). Both these Salmon were considerably older than one from the River Add, the first recorded Salmon to have four spawning-marks on its scales; it was caught as a kelt, and had therefore spawned five times. Unlike the Maree and Canadian fish, it had spawned as a grilse and in every year after and was only eight years old at death.

A large number of kelts have been marked in this country; they generally return to spawn to the rivers in which they were marked. In Eire, over 22,000 kelts had been marked up to 1946, and 527 recaptured. 486 or 90·2 per cent of these were caught either in the river where they were marked, or in its estuary. The remainder were caught in other rivers. So mended kelts, like maiden fish, seem to show a strong but not an absolutely over-riding tendency to return to their native rivers.

In Canada, Huntsman (1938, 1945) found that fish liberated as kelts tend to stay in the estuary, and usually are to be found nearer fresh water than virgin fish. It will be remembered that in the areas investigated by Huntsman some of the smolts and the Salmon into which they grow do not move out of the zone of influence of the river. But during high floods, if they are swept out of the estuary, they seem to lose contact with their spawning stream, and only then do they tend to wander away from the stream in which they first spawned.

It used to be believed that kelts, once in the sea, moved far away from their river, but Huntsman (1945) has found that they sometimes turn round and ascend the river from which they have just descended. This upstream movement is apparently dependent on freshets, and a kelt in the sea may be induced to ascend a different river should a freshet occur whilst it is passing through the zone of influence of that river. Huntsman concludes that the return of kelts to the river is independent of the state of the gonads. It is, however, most unlikely that these fish could have ascended the river for any distance, and inconceivable that they could have spawned again, without a period of feeding and recuperation in the sea. It would be rash indeed to generalize from these very exceptional cases.

According to Huntsman (and others), the time that Salmon spend in the sea between successive spawnings varies considerably, though in some rivers there is much less variation than in others. Despite the paucity of the data, Huntsman feels that even a fragmentary picture is useful at this stage, and his provisional conclusion is that the time spent in the sea by adult Salmon, virgin or spent, is dependent upon the temperature of the sea; if the temperature is low the absence is long. Where the water is stratified into layers of warm and cold water, the fish may have a long or a short absence according to which layer they inhabit. Huntsman's theory, if substantiated, would go far to explain the anomaly of long- and short-absence fish from the same river, and the fact that short-absence fish may become long-absence fish before their third spawning, and conversely. Yet it seems that generally spring fish adopt the long-absence habit and that summer fish spawners return to the sea for a shorter stay.

Among the fish returning to the sea is a small class of those which have migrated normally upstream but have not spawned. They go down to sea with gonads full, and have been called *baggots* or *rawners*. Such fish are usually females full of unshed ova; it is not known whether they have failed to attract a mate or whether they suffer from a stenosis (constriction) of the genital aperture which makes the passage of eggs impossible. Menzies claims that baggots can be stripped by hand, and therefore there can be no serious abnormality. But this is a narrow view. As we have seen in Chapter 6, p. 92, a female salmon cannot shed her eggs until she has made her nest and induced a male to join her in it. "Unattractive" behaviour resulting from hormone deficiency would be a physical abnormality as adequate as stenosis to cause egg-retention, and as likely.

I have not seen many baggots; the few that I have seen have been caught by rod as clean fish in spring, but have been full of eggs and the source of some worry to their catchers. Usually the eggs have by that time shown some signs of being reabsorbed, they were collapsed and rather squarish, and some newly developing very small eggs could be seen in the emptied and collapsed ovary. It is not known what proportion of fish drop down from the spawning beds in this condition, but I think it is very small.

Physical differences enable us to differentiate between a previous spawner and a virgin fish. First, the previous spawners are not truly silvery, but have a golden sheen on their scales, (though unfortunately some late-arriving virgin fish may also have this golden sheen). Secondly, the previous spawners generally have many more spots, especially on the back and gill-covers, than the virgins. Thirdly, the previous spawners in-variably have gill-maggots on their gills; these parasites, which are picked up in fresh water, stay on the gills whilst the fish is in the sea, and return with the fish to fresh water. (See Appendix III, p. 158). And fourthly, the scales of the previous spawners show a spawning-mark.

The main conclusion to be drawn from this brief chapter is that kelts are worth preserving. Their downstream journey should be made as easy as possible; they should not be allowed to remain stranded in eddies, weirs, or above hydroelectric dams. It might even be worth while to net the spawning grounds and transport the kelts down-river to brackish water.

CHAPTER 9

THE SALMON RIVER

ONCE upon a time, and not so very long ago at that, when every suitable river held salmon past counting, no one troubled to consider what made a river suitable or how its suitability could be preserved. It is only three hundred years since Walton wrote:- "And next I shall tell you that it is observed by Gesner and others that there is no better salmon than in England: and that though some of our northern counties have as fat and as large as the River Thames yet none are of so excellent a taste." It does not appear that anglers or fishermen were then subject to much restriction or that Walton himself needed to ask permission to fish where he pleased; there was more than enough for all. But barely a hundred years after Walton's death, bloody battles were being fought on the Solway over Salmon rights. A hundred years later still, Salmon had vanished from the Thames and from many of our northern rivers, never to return; and the condition of our natural water-supplies was becoming a matter of public concern, though more on account of the danger to public health than the discomfiture of anglers.

Since the beginning of the industrial revolution and the rapid increase in population which accompanied it, the threat to salmon rivers has increased enormously—the threefold threat of obstruction, pollution and abstraction. All these, it is important to remember, are natural features of any river; even without human intervention, all rivers are in some degree obstructed and polluted, and from all water is abstracted by evaporation and seepage. Damage to a river system only ensues when the total effect of these agencies passes (it may be but for a short time) a limit of tolerance which the combined efforts of chemists, engineers and legal draftsmen over the last hundred years have failed to specify precisely. In the days of *laisser-faire* it was naturally difficult for anyone to realise that a miller or a canal-builder had not an absolute right to dam a river where he pleased, that streams were not a gift of an all-seeing Providence for the express purpose of sewage disposal, and that the supply of natural water was not inexhaustible. It was extremely difficult for any culprit to accept that what he did was harmful or at least that the harm was not trivial and outweighed by consequent benefits to others as well as to himself. It was usually quite impracticable to bring home particular damage to a particular source.

It needed the threat of cholera and typhoid epidemics in the middle of the nineteenth century to ensure that to-day, in spite of the difficulties consequent on the increase of population and the absorption of the countryside into towns, we enjoy a superb supply of domestic water, palatable, extraordinarily cheap and the safest in the world. It is the fact that we are now using a considerable fraction of our total rainfall and are approaching the point where a single dry season would be a major catastrophe, which is necessitating to-day an agonizing reappraisal of our water resources. One of the first-fruits of this reappraisal has been the River Boards, created by Act of Parliament in 1948 and given additional powers by a further Act in 1951. Each of these Boards is entrusted with the duty of making, and in a large measure of implementing, a unified policy for water utilisation in the whole catchment area allotted to it, including tidal estuaries. No one can suppose that this will prove an easy task, but it has become for the first time a possible one, and the growing public realisation that rivers are national assets, not to be wasted or spoilt by any sectional interest, should be a help. But it is not by spectacular litigation, by appeals to public opinion, or by an ostentatious use of the powers that Parliament has given it, that the success of a River Board will be measured. These may prove to be necessary, but by themselves they will fail as certainly as they have failed in the past.

It is not tactics, but a long-term strategy which is needed, and action which is preventive rather than remedial. Nothing can be done, even if it were desirable to attempt it, to prevent the infiltration into a catchment area of new towns, new hydro-electric works, new power-stations, new reservoirs, new industries: but a great deal can be done to prevent their damaging the rivers: and to do it at a price our country can afford requires action before any new enterprise has left the drawing-board, or better still, before it is properly on it. Once the lesson is learned by the promoters of such enterprises that endless expense and trouble can be saved by full and early consultation with a knowledgeable River Board, there will no longer be occasion for ruinous and futile litigation.

The greatest hindrance to effective action by the River Boards (and especially by their Fishery Committees) is lack of accurate information. The paucity of reliable records is appalling. At the best they may show a trend, up or down, over a few years of the numbers and size of the salmon population with the barest indication of possible causes. At the worst they may amount only to a few fishy stories which not even other anglers are prepared to credit. It is only beginning to be realised that the treatment of a river requires as much skill and experience as the treatment of a human patient, and is as dependent on accurate diagnosis and a full case-history if the river is to be kept alive and restored to health. A post-mortem examination is another matter: though even there it is possible for the amateur to draw wildly wrong conclusions.

This chapter is concerned with some of the methods of treatment which have had a certain effect in the past, or which appear to promise well for the future—provided always that the diagnosis has been right and that the treatment is appropriate to the condition treated. It is fortunate indeed that the first essential quality of a good salmon river, namely clean water and plenty of it, is also, directly or indirectly, a requirement of every water-user. It can therefore be taken for granted that the maintenance and improvement of an existing salmon fishery will always be an integral part of the policy of the River Board concerned.

There are, however, a number of other conditions which a

good salmon river must satisfy. There must be resting pools at reasonably short intervals throughout the length of the river and its tributaries. Impassable barriers must be removed or circumvented. There must be good and ample spawning-beds and good nursery-grounds with an abundance of natural food and, if necessary, a limitation of predators. There must be an adequate but not excessive growth of water-plants of the right kinds. And finally, there must be a generous provision of well-paid, responsible and knowledgeable bailiffs, not only to prevent poaching and unlicensed fishing (often considered more important than in fact they are), but to assess and record the day-to-day condition of the river and to detect, interpret and report on any deviation from normality which might indicate impending trouble. Many other arduous duties fall to their lot, as the following pages show, but the first is to be the eyes, ears and noses of the River Board and its scientific officers.

The struggle for clean water and plenty of it is substantially the struggle against pollution and abstraction, but these threats can rarely be considered independently of each other or of the third threat to salmon, that of obstruction. For, if pollution can be reduced, more abstraction is permissible; and, if abstraction is increased, obstruction by dams may be necessary in order to provide an adequate flow in dry weather; and, if the river is never allowed to fall very low, pollution does less damage.

On most rivers, however, pollution is still clearly the central problem. Space does not permit a full discussion of the variety of pollution, which is almost infinite (cf. Pentelow, 1953; Turing, 1952; Wisdom, 1956; Hynes (in the press). There are two main kinds: pollution by substances which are inherently poisonous, and pollution by substances which, though not directly toxic, suffocate the river by depriving it of dissolved oxygen. Inadequately treated sewage effluent belongs to the second class; industrial wastes may belong to either or both.

The treatment of sewage is now generally so excellent that it is unusual for the effluent to do much harm if adequately diluted. After all London's drinking water contains a fair proportion of sewage effluent. The exceptions occur where a town has grown beyond the capacity of its sewage-plant, leaving no room for it to expand proportionately except at prohibitive expense. Recently two new factors have become important. Because most sewage-plants are working so close to the limit of their capacity, the presence of large quantities of non-soapy detergents in sewage is a matter for serious concern: for, in addition to causing unsightly foaming, these detergents both reduce the efficiency of treatment and increase the deleterious effect of the effluent. The second new factor is the increasing scale of withdrawal of river-water for cooling purposes and its return to the river at a higher temperature. Apart from the fact that cooling-water is sometimes excessively chlorinated and therefore very poisonous, the consequent rise in temperature of the river, if not itself lethal, accentuates the effects of any polluting substances from other source and may alone be a bar to up and downstream movements of fish.

It cannot be too strongly emphasized that an amount of pollution which is ordinarily innocuous may have extremely serious effects if a period of reduced river-flow coincides, as it often does, with a period of hot weather. And it is at such times that an accidental overspill is particularly disastrous. It is necessary to impress on riverside industries that it is not enough for the *average* quantity and quality of their effluent to conform to their River Board's regulations. In addition they should be expected to make every effort to restrict their output of effluent when the river is low and to tighten up supervision so that the probability of accidental spills becomes negligible. Indeed the universal adoption of a practice whereby River Boards notify all riverside industries in their area of the beginning and end of such danger periods would have an excellent effect.

*   *   *

The problem of whether a river can be improved by stocking and the related problem of whether it is worth while to maintain a hatchery on every major tributary are still without any general solution. There is no doubt that a great deal of nonsense has been talked about the advantages of "introducing new blood": it is, in fact, probable that most salmon rivers, if they are not unduly interfered with, are self-regulating, and support about the optimum number of fry and parr. In such cases "stocking" with young fish from elsewhere may actually be deleterious, while stripping native fish, raising the product in a hatchery and returning them to the river as alevins or fry may have no beneficial effect commensurate with the expense.

This picture may, however, be entirely changed by an accident such as a landslip or a bad overspill of pollution, or by the kind of public water-utilisation works which are everywhere becoming more common. Dredging, considered necessary for flood-prevention, may destroy spawning beds and nursery grounds either temporarily or permanently. Conservation and power dams may drown some spawning-grounds and make many others completely inaccessible. In such circumstances restocking may be the only way of maintaining a salmon river; and then the local existence of hatcheries and of men with experience in operating them may more than justify their cost.

It is easy to build and run a hatchery if the problem of water-supply can be overcome. Hatcheries are best built in accessible places where there is an ample and permanent supply of clean, cold water, well-oxygenated and nearly neutral (pH 6-8). It is advantageous to have cold water because it retards hatching, so that, when the alevins are ready for planting out, the conditions in the river are more favourable for them. If the young have to be planted out as early as February, the river is more likely to be in flood and it may not be possible to find places in which they can stay. If they have to be held back and fed in the hatchery new difficulties will have to be faced; scrupulous cleanliness, frequent inspection and the speedy removal of excess food, dead bodies and other debris are necessary if heavy mortality is to be avoided. And, as they grow, the fish must be thinned out and dispersed over a larger number of troughs. It will be remembered that young salmonids prefer live and moving food, but it is difficult to supply this in sufficient quantity in a hatchery, so that the growth-rate there is probably much less than maximal. Mr. Myers, who has had a great deal of experience in modern hatchery practice, is convinced that hatching troughs are always over-crowded and that this results in poorer fish. He has also found that fry fed on natural foods (lake plankton) as distinct from minced raw liver, dried fine whale-meat, etc., put on much more weight than those fed on dead food.

In choosing a site for a hatchery, it is important that a supply of spawning fish should be easily available nearby. Spawning fish can be caught in traps built in association with weirs, and must be stored in keeping-tanks until ready for stripping. Over-crowding in keeping-tanks is not important if there is an abundant flow of clean water through the tanks, but diseased fish must be removed and healthy ones tested frequently for ripeness. This is done by netting small batches of fishes out of the big keeping-tanks into a smaller tank also supplied with abundant running water. Each fish is sexed, and then placed on a grooved flat board or platform, the grooving conforming to the shape of the fish. Pressure is applied to the flank of the fish, and, if eggs or sperm can be pressed out easily, the fish is ready for stripping (the artificial removal of eggs or sperm). When first placed on the stripping-board, the fish struggle and the eggs and sperm are held back; pressure should not be applied until the fish are relaxed. Ripe fish are thus segregated from unripe or hard fish: it is often possible with experience to tell a ripe fish by holding it head down and feeling the belly.

When enough fish are ready for stripping, the following operations are performed, with a team of three or four (Plate 12a, p. 129). A female is placed on the stripping-board and all her eggs forced out into a clean basin; the female is then thrown back into the river. A male is next placed on the stripping-board and two or three "squirts" of sperm forced into the basin. The eggs and sperm are mixed by hand and left covered; and after about five minutes the excess of sperm is washed off. The fertilized eggs are either covered up again or put in a large, lidded container containing fresh water. It is believed that sunshine is harmful to the eggs, but I do not know whether this is really so. If any blood is passed out of the fish during the stripping operation, it should be washed off immediately, and the affected batch of eggs kept separate, as it has been found that such eggs often have a high mortality.

The stripping-board, though hallowed by custom, can be dispensed with. The fish may be held head up by inserting two fingers into the gill-cavity, and the eggs, if ripe enough, will almost drop out of her. It is sometimes claimed that less damage is done to the fish when the stripping-board is not used.

The fertilized eggs must be transported to the hatchery within the next few hours. Here they are laid in trays, of which the floors may be made of perforated zinc or of parallel glass rods: the trays are suspended in long troughs through which run between one and two gallons a minute of clean, cold water. Whether glass rods or zinc is used in hatcheries is, I think, immaterial, provided that oxygenated water can move freely round the eggs. The hatching of eggs in gravel in hatchery troughs has been advocated and it is claimed that when this method is used the mortality is less and the alevins are bigger, but the difficulty of inspection and the danger of infection is certainly increased, and the evidence in favour is unconvincing.

Big eggs hatch into big alevins, and, though many have believed that the initial size-advantage can be persistent, the importance for hatchery keepers of definite confirmation is obvious (Rudd, 1946). Higgs (1942) showed that it was possible and practicable to grade the eggs of the Kamloops trout (*Salmo gairdnerii*) and that fry from the larger eggs held their advantage for more than seven months; so, by segregating the graded eggs, the much more laborious grading and segregation of young fish at a later stage can be eliminated.

*　　　　　*　　　　　*

The treatment of obstruction may require any of three rather different approaches, depending on the magnitude of the job. In this country very many weirs are still standing regardless of the fact that the mills which they supplied with water have long been derelict: most of them could be removed with benefit to the river. Where this is impracticable and in the case of other minor obstacles, it will usually be desirable to make some kind of a pass or ladder. Paradoxically this may sometimes be achieved by making another obstacle downstream of the first so as to deepen the pool and raise the water-level at its foot: but no general rules can be laid down and each case should be treated empirically with full regard to local circumstances and in the confident expectation that the first design may have to be modified in the light of experience (cf. Pryce-Tannat, 1938). It must be remembered that salmon must not only be able to negotiate the pass but induced to use it. Neglect of the one sure guiding principle, namely, that salmon will try to go up where most water is coming down, has often considerably reduced the usefulness of passes which in other respects appeared entirely satisfactory. I have seen an excellent fish-pass in Sweden, complete with an electric fish-counter, lying idle whilst salmon in hundreds were trying to swim up a steep apron to one of the sluices in a big dam, because it was passing more water than the fish-pass.

A radically different approach is required for major obstacles such as the dams associated with power-stations and reservoirs. In the first place a careful survey is required to establish whether enough spawning-gravel will be left undrowned to make it worthwhile to help salmon past the dam. If not, hatcheries on an appropriate scale, supplemented by stew-ponds if the natural nursery-grounds have also been severely curtailed, are the only expedient if the stock is to be maintained. If, on the other hand, the spawning-beds above the dam are still worth exploiting, the alternatives are a ladder of conventional type (which, in the case of a high dam, may have to be of enormous length), or some type of automatic lift. The choice is the more alarming because neither can yet be said to have proved its worth and because second thoughts are likely to be extremely expensive.

Lifts or elevators have been installed fairly extensively in North America where there are very high dams. Many of them consist of an endless chain of saucer-shaped buckets. The salmon are induced (often by means of an electric barrage) to enter the holding-pool at the foot of the lift; from this pool they are automatically scooped up and eventually tipped out above the dam.

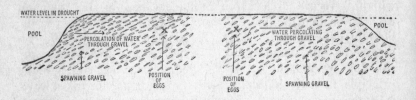

FIG. 16. An ideal spawning ford

Another type of automatic pass, employing the lock principle, may be seen on the Liffey in Eire. Here the dam is only about 60 ft. high; the pass is, in effect, a sloping tunnel about 44 ft. long which is closed automatically at its lower end at appropriate intervals. When the bottom end is closed, the tunnel fills and the fish move up with the water and can swim out above the dam: when it is open, the outrush of water attracts salmon into the bottom of the tunnel. (O'Meallain, 1951).

*   *   *

The productivity of a salmon river depends largely on its spawning-grounds, which vary greatly both in extent and quality from river to river. Ideally spawning fords are areas of gravel of two feet or more in depth, sloping gently downstream, with large pools at either end. The depth of water over such a ford should be about two feet, though Salmon will spawn in as little as six inches of water, and may spawn successfully in four feet or more if the current at this depth is fast enough. (See Fig. 16, above).

The pools serve a two-fold purpose, as safe resting places where also the preliminary courtship can take place, and as reservoirs of water which will percolate downstream through the gravel from one pool to the other. The survival of salmon eggs and fry is dependent upon this percolation of water over the eggs. It is clear from fig. 16, p. 146, that even in periods of drought when the gravel surface of the redd is uncovered water will still pass through it. That this actually happens has been confirmed by examining redds in the observation-tank. In order to collect the eggs the main flow of water was cut off, exposing the surface of the gravel and leaving the pool full of water; a trickle of water flowing over the eggs was clearly visible.

The constitution of spawning gravel varies greatly; generally a bucketful of spawning gravel will contain two or three large stones, much gravel (stones up to 1-2 inches in length) and some silt. The part played in the spawning act by the larger stones has been described in Chapter 5.

Many rivers have areas of gravel apparently suitable as spawning-grounds which are yet never used by spawning salmon. Such gravels may be too "hard" (or cemented) to be moved by the cutting of the female salmon. Hard areas of gravel are formed when many floods remove the finer gravel and the larger stones remaining become compacted. Dredging operations which remove pools, bends and rocks, and thus allow a more rapid run-off will produce areas of compacted gravel. In other instances the cementing may be due to the nature of the silt. Quite often usable spawning gravel is exposed on removal of the hard upper crust, in such cases it might be of value to hoe these areas just before the spawning season.

Soft, or moving gravel, is often found in patches deposited by floods at the upstream end of pools usually on the inner bend of the river. Such gravels lack the larger rocks which anchor the finer gravels and thus they move readily. A female salmon cutting in this type of gravel would find bed-making almost impossible, rather like trying to make a hole in dry sand.

A few weeks after spawning the only indication (from the bank) that salmon have spawned on a ford are patches of clean gravel. These are areas of gravel which have been disturbed by the female and have as a result lost their covering of silt or plant growth: at the same time the cleaner lower gravels are exposed.

On closer examination it will be seen that a recently vacated redd is in the form of a hump of gravel which is sloping gradually upstream to a hole. In the generalized redd figured (Fig. 17) five batches of eggs (marked X) have been deposited and covered up in succession. The hole or depression at the upstream end of the redd marks the area from which the female removed gravel to cover up her last batch of eggs. The eggs will be found in batches

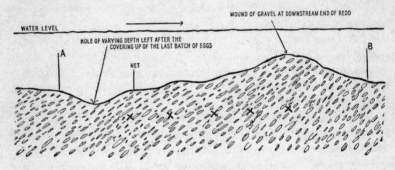

FIG. 17. A redd

of a thousand or so downstream from this point (see fig. 17). To collect the eggs a fine-meshed hand-net should be placed about one to one-and-a-half feet downstream of the hole and the gravel removed carefully to a depth of at least six inches. A few stray eggs may be seen before the main batch is exposed, or they may pass unnoticed into the net, so it is important to examine its contents periodically. Most of the eggs in a batch will generally be found under two or three substantial stones (up to six inches in diameter). Other batches of eggs will be found in succession downstream at intervals of about a foot and a half. The last batches of eggs to be exposed may be covered by one-and-a-half to two feet of gravel.

The available area of gravel suitable for spawning is frequently a limiting factor for the salmon population of a river; and it is very readily reduced not only directly and obviously by dredging but indirectly: for spawning gravel can only persist between not very widely separated limits of current. Every scheme for increasing or reducing obstructions in a river should therefore be investigated from this standpoint, and its probable consequences, both direct and indirect, assessed before embarking on it.

* * *

The need for fishable reaches in any salmon river is obvious. Good fishing reaches are dependent not only on the presence of resting pools, but often also on the control of bankside vegetation and in some cases the control of water-weed. As in circumventing obstacles, so in creating pools it is often necessary for man to improve on nature: and generally this is neither difficult nor expensive. Sometimes dredging is required, but it often suffices to make a partial obstruction and so induce the river to scour out a deeper channel. Here, too, no general rules can be laid down.

Not many of our salmon rivers suffer from an excess of weed, though in some, the Hampshire Avon for example, it is a major problem. Here its growth affects the water-level and the rate of flow, and thus has a secondary effect on the upstream migration of salmon. Weed-beds tend to silt up, and the extent and suitability of spawning areas may be seriously restricted in consequence. But in compensation, in southern rivers the amount of fish-food to be found sheltering in the weed is very great indeed. When I was working on these rivers I began an investigation into the fauna of the main types of weed to discover whether one species of weed was preferable to another. It was broken off by the War, but not before some interesting results had emerged. Six species of weed were chosen: *Ranunculus pseudofluitans*, water crowfoot; *Oenanthe sp.*, river dropwort; *Apium nodiflorum*, water celery; *Callitriche stagnalis*, starwort; *Hippuris vulgaris*, mare's-tail; and *Glyceria fluitans*, watergrass. Equal volumes of these six species of weed were taken in each month from October to May inclusive, from the sides of the stream, and from deeper water in midstream. Even though the work was not completed, it was clear that the faunas of different weeds differ substantially. From the fisherman's point of view, it appears that some of the weeds could well be dispensed with; for example, starwort and watergrass. Starwort carries a varied and rich fauna, but it is also a bad mud-collector, and if present in any quantity soon causes serious silting. It should be cultivated, if at all, only in small batches. No great loss would occur if it were excluded completely, for all its invertebrate inhabitants are present in other weeds such as *Ranunculus* and *Hippuris*. *Hippuris* is an excellent weed to have in a river, as its shape is such that it collects no mud, and yet it carries a very full complement of fish-foods, such as uncased caddis (*Polycentropus*); blackfly (*Simulium*); midges (*Chironomus*); and may-fly (*Baëtis*); as well as the freshwater shrimp (*Gammarus*) and the water-louse (*Asellus*). Mare's-tail, however dense, will not slow down the stream as much as water buttercup or water celery. I suggest that River Boards with weed troubles might try exterminating other weeds and planting mare's-tail.

Excessive weed has to be cut at intervals, and the cutting is always an expensive business and may be a danger to the river if it is not done with discretion. Destruction of weed by cutting results also in the destruction of a great deal of fish-food, including the diatoms and small sessile algae on which many fry feed; it suddenly destroys the principal refuge of small fishes; and it may have a disastrous effect in deoxygenating the water of the river. It has been shown that weeds assist very considerably in the oxygenation of the water and in the cleaning-up of a stream polluted by some types of effluent; Berry (1932-33) believes that the sudden cutting of weeds at a time of drought and high temperature makes the oxygen-reducing types of pollution especially dangerous, even though normally they are present at a "safe" concentration. Moreover, large banks of cut weed tend to collect at weirs and themselves become a source of pollution as they decay.

Berry, faced with the weed problem on the Avon, was a strong advocate of chemical weed-control as opposed to cutting. Obviously, the weed-killer must be harmless to fish, fish-eggs, and fish-food. Sodium arsenite appears to be satisfactory; in appropriate concentration it is said (Wiebe, 1930) to destroy submerged plants without injury to fish or the destruction of appreciable quantities of microscopic or macroscopic food organisms. Berry (1935-36) carried out successful large-scale experiments with arsenical weed-killers in the south of England and in Scotland, and some work on this problem has also been done in the United States. Spiers (1948) gives a summary of the literature on aquatic weed-control.

Tower-Coston *et al.* (1936) give a list of water-weeds and make suggestions as to what to grow in various types of streams, what part of the stream they should be planted in, and what planting methods to adopt.

*　　　*　　　*

We are still a long way from being able to give a general rational answer to the fundamental question: why does not a given salmon river carry more salmon than in fact it does?

It is true that we can sometimes (after the event) associate a decline in the salmon population with an increase in some factor known to be deleterious, such as obstruction or pollution. We can sometimes recognize a correlation between a change in the character of the salmon population (*e.g.* an increase in the ratio of grilse to spring fish) and alterations to the character of the river as a result of human intervention. In consequence we tend to grasp over-hastily at any explanation which is plausible without taking the trouble (and often going to the very considerable expense) of ascertaining whether it is right; and we tend on the other hand to ignore phenomena which we cannot explain.

We do not know why the River Wye became a spring-fish river without apparent human intervention; we must conclude that the failure of all attempts to produce a spring-fish river by intention implies that they have been based on erroneous assumptions, but we are still far from being able to make a plan which would be likely to succeed.

Some inferences can tentatively be drawn from earlier chapters in this book. One of these is that the limitation on numbers of salmon has a different origin in northern and southern rivers. In the former it is probably lack of food for fry and parr: in the latter it is more likely to be lack of spawning-grounds with a consequent high mortality of eggs. Another possible inference is that the relative numbers of spring and summer fish, and of sea-age groups in general, is dependent on the geographical distribution of spawning-beds and nursery-grounds within the river system under consideration.

But inferences such as these are still remote and uncertain: the immediate need is for more research and more reliable information. All the evidence is consistent with the belief that it is what happens to a salmon between the egg and smolt stages which determines its future; but we do not know what this is in anything like enough detail, and until recently there was no way of finding out. The methods of sampling and the introduction of the electric fishing-machine (which stuns fish without causing permanent injury), bring within reach the making of the adequate census without which only guess-work is possible.

*   *   *

When a lady enquired of Doctor Johnson why, in his Dictionary, he had wrongly defined the pastern of a horse, he replied, "Ignorance, Madam, plain ignorance." His candour cost him nothing and enhanced his reputation for independence and integrity. I have little doubt that the King of Fish would be more secure in his kingdom if experts of all kinds—chemists, water-engineers, biologists and anglers of great experience—were less afraid to confess that they do not know.

APPENDIX I

Specific Characteristics and Hybrids

THE two species of the genus *Salmo* in our waters are the Atlantic Salmon, *Salmo salar,* and the brown and sea trout, *Salmo trutta,* which includes all our trouts, migratory and non-migratory; these used to be separated into *Salmo fario,* non-migratory, and *Salmo trutta,* migratory.

Salmon and trout are very closely related, so much so that it is not always easy to differentiate between a young Salmon (parr) and a young trout. The specific characters of these young fish as defined by Gunther (1864), Day (1887), Regan (1911) and Nall (1930) fall into three groups (Jones, 1947).

a. Spotting and colour of various parts of the body.
b. Relative size of various parts of the body.
c. Counts of scales, fin-rays and pyloric caeca.

It is not advisable to use only the first group of characters; they are unreliable and can vary considerably even in fish from the same river. Figure 1, p. 4 shows the main morphological differences between young Salmon and trout.

The differences can be tabulated as follows (Jones, 1947):

a. SPOTTING AND COLOUR OF VARIOUS PARTS OF THE BODY

Character	Salmon	Trout
1. Colour of the adipose fin.	Rarely edged with red.	Usually edged with red.
2. Colour of the pectoral and pelvic fins.	Generally grey.	Generally orange-yellow.
3. Spotting of the body.	Usually sparsely spotted.	Usually heavily spotted.
4. Spotting of the operculum.	Rarely more than three spots.	Often more than three spots.
5. Spotting of the dorsal fin.	Spots poorly defined.	Spots generally well defined.
6. Parr-marks (vertical dark bars) on body.	Usually 11-12.	Usually 9-10, often disappearing after first or second year.

b. RELATIVE SIZE OF VARIOUS PARTS OF THE BODY

1. Relative length of
   maxillae.

   a. at body length 4″.   Maxillae extend to   Maxillae extend to
                             centre of the pupil of   posterior edge of the pupil
                             the eye.   of the eye.

   b. at body length 6″.   Maxillae extend to the   Maxillae extend to the
                             posterior edge of the   posterior edge of the iris.
                             pupil.

2. Thickness (or height)   Slender, i.e. height of   Thick, i.e. height of wrist
   of "wrist" (caudal   wrist is about one-tenth   is at least one-eighth of
   peduncle) from dorsal   of the length of the   the length of the body.
   to ventral surface.   body.

3. Forking of the tail.   Deeply forked, with   Shallowly forked, with
                           middle tail-rays not   middle tail-rays three-
                           more than three-fifths   fifths (or more) the length
                           of the longest rays.   of the longest rays.

c. COUNTS OF SCALES, FIN-RAYS AND PYLORIC CAECA

1. Number of scales   10 to 13, usually 11.   13 to 16, usually 14,
   from the posterior   rarely 12.
   edge of the adipose
   fin downwards and
   forwards to the lateral
   line (the "scale-
   count" area).

2. Number of rays in the   10 to 12, usually 11.   8 to 10, usually 9.
   dorsal fin.

3. Number of pyloric   50 to 80.   30 to 60.
   caeca.

From the above it is clear that one cannot certainly differentiate between a young Salmon and a young trout unless several of the above characters are checked. For instance, it is not safe to assume that because a fish is very spotted, it must be a trout. Unfortunately this is just what fishermen do; and it results in a considerable wastage of young Salmon.

Once a Salmon has been down to the sea it is fairly easy to tell it from a trout by the following characteristics:

a. Salmon have few (four in grilse) vomerine teeth (teeth on the vomer or hard palate). Trout and sea-trout have more (eleven). This, however, is not a reliable characteristic as these teeth tend to drop out in older fish.

b. Scale-count—a much more satisfactory test.

c. Dorsal fin-ray count.

d. Caudal peduncle or "wrist"—quite a useful characteristic which can be used when handling living fish; the wrist of the Salmon is narrower and easily grasped even when the fish is large, whereas large trout and sea-trout slip through one's fingers. The height of the wrist in fish weighing three to five pounds is one-fifteenth to one-sixteenth of the total length in Salmon, and about one-tenth or one-eleventh in trout of the same weight.

e. Examination of the scales for age, spawning, etc., often confirms the results of such an examination (see Chapter 3, p. 43).

But it is not always easy to tell the difference even between adult Salmon and trout, and it is possible to reach a wrong conclusion if only a part of the evidence is examined. This was shown recently (1954) when a record "trout" was caught in the River Nadder; examination of the scales showed that the fish was a Salmon (see Chapter 4, Plate 5e, p. 52).

As there appears to be such a close relationship between Salmon and trout, it has often been suggested that the two species may interbreed in nature. Personally, I have never seen a natural hybrid between Salmon and trout, though I have handled many thousands of both species, nor have I heard or read of any authentic natural hybrid. It must, however, be emphasized that a hybrid would not be easily recognisable, and would almost certainly escape notice on a cursory examination.

However, some years ago I had the opportunity of examining in detail some hybrids produced artificially by crossing female Salmon and male brown trout; this was done by Mr. Skinner for Sir Ernest Wills and a detailed account of these fish has been published (Jones, 1947). Mr. Skinner made several crosses and I was able to examine yearling, two-year-old, and four-year-old hybrids, as well as a back-cross between a female hybrid and a male Salmon. It was obvious that unless examined very carefully such hybrids would be called trout because of their trout-like markings and colouration. Examination of the yearling hybrids showed that in fact seven trout characters were common to all the fish, five concerned with colour and spotting, the other two being height of the wrist, and the number of scales along the scale-count line. Tail-shape and weak spotting of the dorsal fin were Salmon characters common to all the fish. The length of the maxillae, the number of rays in the dorsal fin, and the number of pyloric caeca were trout-like in some of the hybrids and Salmon-like in others. The two-year-old hybrids were even more trout-like in general appearance; they had only one salmon characteristic in common, the unsatisfactory one of colour of pectoral and pelvic fins. The four-year-old hybrids were also trout-like in general appearance. Salmon characteristics were naturally more prevalent in the back-cross hybrids; the dorsal fin-ray count, the forking of the tail and the spotting of operculum were Salmon-like in all. Day also (1887) lists several instances of artificially produced hybrids though he does not mention natural hybrids.

Reciprocal artificial crosses (between male Salmon and female trout) have been less frequently recorded; the percentage fertilization is said to be quite low (not more than 40 per cent), possibly because of the mechanical difficulties resulting from a large sperm trying to enter a small micropyle (the small hole through which a sperm enters an egg). Alm (1955) investigated a considerable number of possible salmonid hybrids. In general the percentage fertilization was lower and the mortality of alevins and fry higher in hybrids than in pure stocks: the growth-rate of the surviving hybrids, on the other hand, was usually intermediate between those of the parent species, but might be better than either. Intergeneric crosses (e.g. *Salmo* x *Salvelinus*) were attended by very high mortality. He did not find that the vigour or the appearance of the hybrids depended to any noticeable extent on which way round the cross was made, though the percentage fertilization was often significantly lower when the mother was much smaller than the father.

Hybrids between Salmon and trout crossed both ways became smolts in two, three, or four years; and marked five-year-old individuals, reared in ponds and released into the Gulf of Bothnia, were recovered, in company with Salmon, at the southern edge of the Baltic Sea more than 500 miles away.

Svärdson (1945) has shown that the diploid number of chromosomes is 60 in *S. salar* and 80 in *S. trutta*. For first-generation hybrids it is, as expected, 70. From a comparison with other salmonids, he concludes that the basic haploid number is 10 and that all living salmonids are high polyploids. This needs further investigation (White, 1954).

Nall has suggested that hybridization in nature may take place in small streams, but in my opinion it could take place equally easily in large streams. When brown trout have been present during the spawning of Salmon in the Salmon observation-tank, the Salmon have almost always driven the trout off the bed; but on one occasion Bailiff Stanley Jones and myself suspected that a brown trout had actually passed out sperm at the same time as a male Salmon parr. I am convinced that under natural conditions in the river it is not impossible for male brown trout to take part in the spawning of adult Salmon, but I am not prepared to assert that it ever happens.

APPENDIX II

Key to the Genera of Salmonidae and the Species of Oncorhynchus

a. GENERA OF SALMONIDAE

1. 13 to 19 branchiostegal rays, 19–40 gill-rakers on the first gill-arch. 13 or more rays in the anal fin   *Oncorhynchus*
   12 or fewer branchiostegal rays, 20 or fewer gill-rakers on the first arch, fewer than 13 (rarely 13) rays in the anal fin.   2

2. Vomer flat, not boat-shaped. Body with dark spots on light background
                                                                        Salmo
   Vomer boat-shaped. Body with light spots on dark background   *Salvelinus*
            (from Blair, Blair, Brodkorb, Cagle and Moore 1957).

b. SPECIES OF ONCORHYNCHUS

I am indebted to Dr. Ethelwyn Trewavas for the following translation from Berg (1932). For anal fin-rays, Roman numerals indicate the number of spiny rays, Arabic numerals that of soft rays.

   a. Not more than 150–160 scales in longitudinal series.
   　b. Not more than 27 gill-rakers in the first arch.
   　　c. Not more than 15 branchiostegal rays, usually less.
   　　　d. Less than 100 pyloric caeca.
   　　　　e. When half-grown, more or less clear dark transverse bars on the body; above and below these bars usually rather coarse round black spots. Anal fin-rays III–IV 11–14 (15); scales along lateral line 130–140; branchiostegal rays 11–15; gill-rakers 18–22; pyloric caeca 35–76.   *O. masou*
   　　　　ee. When half-grown no dark bars or spots on body (there are fine round spots). Anal fin-rays IV–V 12–14; scales along lateral line 120–140; branchiostegal rays 13–14; gill-rakers 19–23; pyloric caeca 45–81.   *O. kisutch*
   　　　dd. Pyloric caeca 135–185. Anal fin-rays III 12–15; scales along lateral line 125–150; branchiostegal rays (11) 12–15; gill-rakers 19–25   *O. keta*
   　　cc. Branchiostegal rays 15–19. Anal fin-rays III 15–16; scales along

lateral line 135–155; gill-rakers 23–27; pyloric caeca 140–185
O. tschawytscha

   bb. Gill-rakers 30–40; Anal fin-rays III–IV 13–15; scales along lateral line
     130–142; branchiostegal rays 13–15; pyloric caeca 75–95   *O. nerka*
aa. Scales smaller 177 to 236 along lateral line; gill-rakers 26–33;
   branchiostegal rays 10–14; Anal fin-rays II–IV 12–16.   *O. gorbuscha*

DISTRIBUTION (From Blair *et al*, and Starr Jordan)

1. *O. masou*   Japan, fairly abundant in streams of Hokkaido (Starr Jordan).
2. *O. kisutch*   From Japan to Alaska and south to Monterey Bay, California, now established in Maine.
3. *O. keta*   From Kamchatka to Alaska and south to San Francisco, California.
4. *O. tschawytscha* From Northern China to Alaska and south to Ventura River, Southern California. Introduced but not established in Maine.
5. *O. nerka*   Japan to Alaska and south to Klamath river, California. Introduced into several states including Maine.
6. *O. gorbuscha* Northern Japan to Alaska and south to La Jolla, California.

APPENDIX III

Some Parasites and Diseases of Salmon

THE known external parasites of Salmon can be conveniently divided into those which attack the fish in fresh water and those which attack them in the sea. The former group includes *Salmincola salmonea* the salmon gill-maggot, *Argulus foliaceus* the fresh-water or carp louse, several leeches of which *Piscicola geometra* is the commonest, and a Trematode worm *Gyrodactylus*. The only important marine parasite is a Crustacean *Lepeophtheirus salmonis*.

a. Salmincola salmonea, the salmon gill-maggot (Figures 18 and 19, pp. 160, 161): This is a common and widespread parasite about which comparatively little was known until Friend (1941) published a full account of its life-history and ecology. The salmon gill-maggot is a copepod crustacean which, like other parasites in its group, including *Argulus* and *Lepeophtheirus*, bears little resemblance to free-living copepods such as Cyclops. The species *salmonea* is, at least in Scotland, confined to Salmon.

As their English name implies, these maggots are found on the gill-filaments of most of the fish, where they may be equally distributed on both sets of gills: there may be a hundred or more on one fish. The adult female and male parasites are illustrated in Figures 18 and 19, pp. 160, 161, the female bears a pair of egg-sacs. Males are much less common than females, and Friend in his whole investigation only saw six. The parasite attaches itself to the adult Salmon in fresh water, and remains on the fish throughout its stay in the sea. Gill-maggots have not been found on parr and smolts, probably because their larvae are too large to pass through the gill-slits of small fish.

Most of the Salmon are infected by the parasite in fresh water. In periods of drought when Salmon are held up in the estuary for two or more weeks, the parasites of infected fish produce eggs which develop into free-swimming larvae and infect other fish. The larvae are killed by sea-water.

The life-history of the parasite is as follows. The eggs hatch in about 14 to 15 days to give free-swimming larvae which may live in this free state for six days. If during this time a larva finds the gills of a Salmon it attaches itself to them by means of gripping appendages and moults into a second larval stage. After a further moult it becomes either a mature male or a

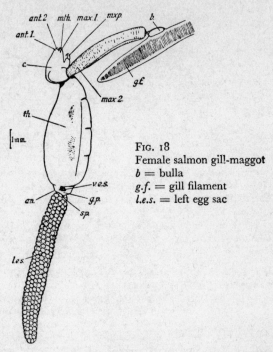

FIG. 18

Female salmon gill-maggot
b = bulla
$g.f.$ = gill filament
$l.e.s.$ = left egg sac

first-stage female: both of these can actually move about on the gills. Copulation takes place at this stage, and after copulation the male dies. Meanwhile the female has developed an attachment organ and can no longer move over the gills: about six months after copulation, eggs are produced. A moult follows and the eggs are extruded: two further sets of eggs may be extruded by the female before the Salmon returns to the sea. If the kelt returns to the sea before these later generations of eggs have been extruded, reproduction is inhibited in the sea and will not be resumed until the fish returns to fresh water. Then the parasite lays its eggs and drops off the gills, presumably dead: the fish is then liable to reinfection.

Figure 20, p. 162, shows how and when a Salmon is infected by the parasite. As it is picked up in fresh water and stays on the fish in the sea, previously-spawned fish returning to the river for a second or a third spawning nearly always carry it. Sometimes these previous spawners (or "Bull Trout" as they are called on the River Tay) have no gill-maggots: in such cases the maggots may have completed their reproductive cycle and dropped off before the fish reached the sea after its first spawning.

The effect of the gill-maggots on the Salmon is not harmful to the fish,

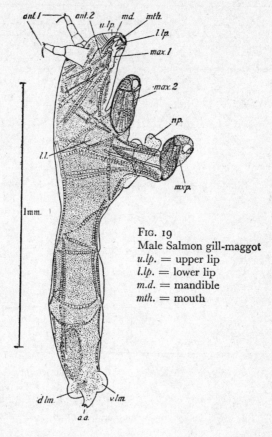

FIG. 19
Male Salmon gill-maggot
u.lp. = upper lip
l.lp. = lower lip
m.d. = mandible
mth. = mouth

unless the infection is very heavy. The amount of blood lost through the blood-sucking habits of the parasite cannot be very great, but on the other hand the lesions produced by gill-maggots when feeding must be regarded as possible sites where infection by bacteria and fungal spores may take place. Some of the mortality of kelts may thus be due to the activity of gill-maggots. As Friend says, although the parasites apparently do no harm, the fish would be better off without them. It is not possible to eliminate these pests completely, but their spread could probably be reduced if efforts were made to prevent fish crowding together in stagnant pools.

b. Argulus foliaceus, the fresh-water or carp louse (Figure 21, p. 163), is an external parasite of fresh-water fish which is sometimes found on Salmon.

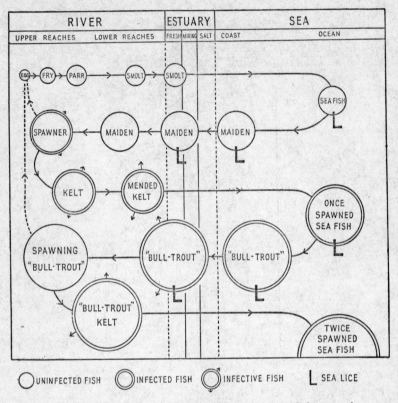

FIG. 20. Diagram showing the life history of the Salmon and its infection by gill-maggots and sea-lice

Hutton states that a Salmon which has been a long time in the river will acquire a considerable number of these parasites. He has seen a diseased Salmon covered with these pests not only all over its surface, but also in its mouth. The parasites attach themselves to the incoming fish as soon as they enter fresh water, and there have been instances recorded of newly arrived fish carrying both the fresh-water louse (*Argulus*) and the sea-louse (*Lepeophtheirus*).

As will be seen from Figure 21, p. 163, these lice are disc-shaped and flat-bodied, and so offer little resistance to the water as the fish swims through it. They attach themselves to their host by two suckers under the front end of the body. These suckers are situated on short muscular stalks which are capable of a limited amount of movement; by alternately releasing the suckers and moving them forward the parasites can change their position on the body of the fish.

The parasites are very transparent; the males are slightly smaller and less conspicuous than the females, which often carry large opaque masses of eggs in the middle of the body.

Between the suckers of *Argulus* is a "poison spine", and just behind them a suctorial mouth or proboscis for sucking food from the host. It is believed to suck the blood of its host, but it has not been established that it does so. The function of the "poison spine" may be to inject a substance which prevents blood-clotting (like the secretion of a mosquito's salivary glands) or to inject enzymes which pre-digest superficial tissue. It is most unlikely that its primary purpose is to poison the host, though the superficial laceration which it inflicts may open a path to infection by pathogenic bacteria and fungus.

c. Lepeophtheirus salmonis, the sea-louse, is a well-known parasite of Salmon. Its presence on a fish is often taken as an indication that the latter has not long left the sea, for the sea-louse lives and breeds in the sea and dies in the river. The eggs hatch in the sea; the larvae swim freely near the surface of the water, and after several moults attach themselves to Salmon. They have no suckers, but the whole hollow flattened body acts as a sucking disc when its

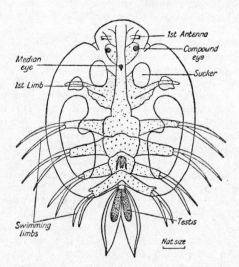

FIG. 21. *Argulus*—the fresh-water louse

margins are pressed against the skin. In addition, two prehensile claws are dug into the flesh and help the parasite to hold on. The females are much larger than the males and have paired egg-sacs. Colman states that sea-lice suck the Salmon's blood.

Hutton (1923) claims that sea-lice have been found on Wye Salmon 120 miles upstream, and he believes that when the river water is cold, sea-lice can survive in it for well over a week.

d. *Gyrodactylus*, a small trematode worm, may sometimes attack Salmon parr (mostly in stew ponds in hatcheries). This worm may attack any part of the body but is usually found on the fins; if the parasites are numerous the fins become frayed, and the lesions can become infected by fungus. If some of the slime on a parasitized fish is scraped off and looked at under a microscope, the little worms can be seen quite easily. Each has at the posterior end of its body a pair of large recurved hooks, and surrounding these is a flattened disc-shaped structure bearing on its outer margin a number of small hooks, by means of which it clings to the host. *Gyrodactylus* gives birth to living young which are already well-developed and attach themselves to the host immediately they are liberated. The parasite can be got rid of by immersing the host for about a minute in a slightly acid bath (one part of glacial acetic acid to five hundred parts of water).

Some of the fresh-water leeches, especially *Piscicola geometra*, are said to attach themselves to Salmon; but the infestation is temporary and seldom if ever heavy. The loss of blood is therefore unlikely to be serious and the injury to the host, if any, is the increased liability to infection through the wound.

Particular reference must be made to furunculosis. It is surprising that so many fishermen and others confuse fungus attack (see later) with furunculosis. Furunculosis is so named because of the development of characteristic "furuncles" or boils. The symptoms of the disease are usually, but not always, well defined. The most obvious is the presence of open sores, usually on the muscles of the back, but sometimes elsewhere: if they appear near the base of the dorsal or pelvic fins the disease may be confused with "fin-rot", an entirely different disease.

The sores originate as small red spots in the subcutaneous tissue or amongst the muscle-fibres. They are full of bacteria, *Bacillus salmonicida*, which multiply rapidly and cause disintegration of the neighbouring blood-vessels and tissues. The bacterium is short, non-motile, Gram-negative (this refers to a staining reaction important for diagnostic purposes) and non-spore-forming. It is not confined to Salmon or to the Salmonidae. The red spots increase in size, and many eventually break through the skin to form open sores, unless, as sometimes happens, the fish dies first. The intestine may also be inflamed and the spleen is enlarged and a bright cherry red, instead of its usual dull red. The intestine is usually congested and a discharge of blood from the anus may be observed. The manifestations of the disease are very variable and in some cases fish showing none of these symptoms have been proved to have died from it. A final identification of the bacteria can only be made by a competent bacteriologist (Williamson, 1928). It is not known how they enter the body. There is no known treatment and the disease is regarded as incurable and fatal, though possibly modern antibiotics might be effective at an early stage.*

A Furunculosis Committee, appointed in 1929, reported in 1930 and 1933. As a result of its recommendations, the Diseases of Fish Act was passed in 1937. This Act, among other things, makes furunculosis a notifiable disease and gives the Minister of Agriculture and Fisheries much the same powers in respect of this disease in fish as he already possessed in respect of foot-and-mouth disease in cattle, namely, powers to designate an infected area, to impose a stand-still on movements of stock and to order its destruction. The Act also prohibits the importation of fresh-water fish except under licence.

The Furunculosis Committee (1930, 1933) in both its reports has stressed the need for further research into the etiology of the disease. The causative organism has been investigated by Griffin, Snieszko, and Friddle (1952) who suggest placing it in a new bacterial genus *Aeromonas*. The consensus of opinion is that infection spreads quickly in adverse conditions, especially in the not uncommon combination of low water, high temperature and over-crowding. But how infection begins is unknown: it is even possible that the bacterium is a common constituent of the flora of the digestive tract, from which virulent strains develop and invade the tissues of weakened fish. Bacteriological identification of the bacterium depends on its morphology, its characteristics when cultured in a laboratory, and its reactions to biochemical tests; a useful feature is the production of a brown pigment under certain specified conditions. It is also possible to make use of its immunological properties for identification, by injecting it into test-animals.

The disease is always contracted in fresh water. Non-infected Salmon coming in from the sea can become infected either from diseased fish or from healthy carriers of the disease: as no spores are produced by the bacterium, infection must be by close contact with infected fish. Such proximity occurs when the rivers are low and the fish confined, and often overcrowded, in pools. The bacterium cannot exist for long as a saprophyte (i.e. live on dead tissue) in fresh water; it is an obligate parasite. It is, however, possible that some increase in number can take place after the death of the infected fish.

One of the most important factors in causing epidemics of furunculosis is water temperature. Healthy carriers may succumb rapidly to the disease if the water temperature rises. Temperature not only affects the pathogenicity of the bacterium, but also its spread. In Britain the danger of epidemics becomes great when the water temperature rises to between 55°F and 65°F.

* According to recent reports from U.S.A. terramycin and chloramphenicol are effective in the treatment of furunculosis in salmonids on fish-farms, but sulphonamides (especially sulphamerazine) are also effective and are preferred for economic reasons. (Snieszko, 1953; Gustell and Snieszko, 1948, 1949).

All concerned with fish and fisheries, and this includes fishermen, should be acquainted with Fisheries Notice No. 30, circulated (free) by the Ministry of Agriculture and Fisheries. This important pamphlet gives an account of the symptoms of the disease, and the procedure to be adopted on finding a fish suspected of being infected. The following is a quotation:—"It is, therefore, essential that fish suspected to be suffering from or to have died of furunculosis should be examined bacteriologically, and arrangements have been made with the Director of the Public Health Laboratory Service for examinations to be carried out free of charge at the laboratories, the addresses of which are given at the end of this leaflet.

"Fish intended for examination should be freshly taken out of the water and no disinfectant or preservative of any kind should be used on either the fish or packing. Preferably fish which are in a dying condition should be selected and the whole fish must be submitted for examination. Specimens should be *taken* to the laboratory by some responsible person. During ordinary office hours on weekdays prior notification is not necessary, but at unusual hours or week-ends, the laboratory should be notified by telephone that a specimen is being submitted.

"The Public Health Laboratory Service will supply a report to the sender of the fish; if he is a private person, he should report any positive findings to the River Board as soon as practicable. River Boards will in all cases consult Fisheries Department of the Ministry of Agriculture and Fisheries when an outbreak has been confirmed."

Fungus disease in Salmon (which, contrary to a not uncommon belief has nothing to do with furunculosis) is usually most prevalent in fish which have been in the river for a long time, and in kelts. The fungus generally involved is *Saprolegnia ferox,* but it is probable that other species also may attack the fish (Davies, 1946). It is now believed that invasion by the fungus is secondary to infection by a bacterium, *Bacillus salmonis pestis,* which enters the fish presumably through a cut or abrasion. The multiplication of the bacteria causes a patch of necrosis and the fungus establishes itself on the dead tissue. Once established, the fungal filaments spread rapidly through the living tissue, as well as growing outside and producing the characteristic fuzzy appearance of fungus disease (Plate 12b and pp. 129).

Saprolegnia may also attack eggs in hatcheries: it develops quickly on eggs damaged by rough handling. Undamaged eggs may be infected by contact with fungused eggs. The fungus reproduces asexually by means of large numbers of minute two-ciliated zoospores which can infect other fishes directly: it also reproduces sexually but this form of reproduction plays little part in spreading the disease.

Salt is probably the best cure. The fish should be removed from the river and dipped in a three per cent solution of common salt until they show signs of distress. It may be necessary in severe infections to repeat the treatment. Potassium permanganate at a dilution of 1 in 100,000 may also be used; the fish can be left in this solution for longer periods. It might well be worth while to adopt as normal river management procedure the netting of all the major spawning grounds and the treatment of all the fungus-covered kelts. A great number of spawning fish might be saved by this treatment.

Another disease prevalent among salmon held up by low water is the so-called White Spot Disease. Small white spots develop on the head of the fish and the eyes may be affected (Calderwood, 1905). Several kinds of bacteria may occur in these white spots. Apparently the only cure is a timely spate (Menzies, 1931).

"Fin-rot", sometimes called "tail-rot", is characterised by the disintegration of the fins. In the Salmon parr that I have seen suffering from this disease, either the dorsal or the caudal fin was the first fin to be affected. The infection spreads to the other fins, and in bad cases they may disappear completely. The first noticeable sign of the disease is a whitish semi-transparent line along the outer margin of the fin. This line gradually moves down along the fin, and the fin edges get frayed owing to the disintegration of the flesh between the fin-rays. In late stages the fin may be entirely destroyed, and sores full of white pus may form at its root. These lesions have often been confused with those of furunculosis, but the discharge in furunculosis is red. Fin-rot, if untreated, is fatal. The cause of the disease is a rod-shaped bacterium. Infected fish can be cured in the early stages of the disease by immersion in a 1 in 2,000 solution of copper sulphate for one to two minutes. Several treatments may be necessary and if the fish is in an advanced stage of attack it is better to destroy it.

"Gill disease" or "gill catarrh", which is principally a hatchery disease, can be quite serious. The fish generally appear to be perfectly normal until a short time before death. In early stages the gills may become congested; later the tips enlarge and the gills become fused together; generally they secrete an abnormal amount of mucus. The disease is due to infection by bacteria, which in this instance are long thread-like filaments. As a result of the fusion of the gills and the secretion of large quantities of mucus, the gills become clogged and respiration is impeded. Treatment by dipping the fish for one minute in a 1 in 2,000 solution of copper sulphate is effective in early stages. In America treatment with a 1 in 400,000 solution of potassium permanganate is standard practice and is said to be very effective. The tanks containing infected trout are flushed with the solution every day for four days: if necessary the four-day treatment is repeated at intervals. More recently it has been said that a single four-hour treatment with P.M.A. (pyridyl mercuric acetate) 2 parts per million is effective (Snieszko, 1953).

APPENDIX IV

Two Methods of Estimating Lengths from Scales

NALL (1930) used the following apparatus as a means of estimating lengths from scales: (1) a projector by means of which an enlarged image of the scale is projected on a flat surface; (2) a number of white cards about $6'' \times \frac{1}{2}''$; (3) a piece of millimetre graph-paper on which two lines are drawn at right angles to each other in one corner: the vertical line is marked off in, say, 5 mm. intervals, and from these points lines are drawn parallel to the horizontal line.

The image of the scale is projected onto the flat surface to a size of not more than six inches, and the card is laid on the image so that one of its corners rests in the middle of the centre ring (or nucleus) of the scale with its length parallel to the long axis of the scale. Holding the card in this position, the end of each winter band of rings is marked on the card, and also the edge of the scale, which may not end in a winter band (Figure 22).

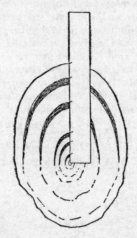

FIG. 22. Diagram of scale with measuring card

The card is then placed on the calculating table. The length of the fish at death is known. The corner of the card which lay in the nucleus of the scale is placed where the vertical and horizontal lines meet, and the final mark on the card (i.e. the edge of the scale-mark), placed so that it cuts the horizontal line representing the length of the fish at death: the intermediate lengths are read off where each mark on the card cuts a horizontal line, as shown in Figure 23.

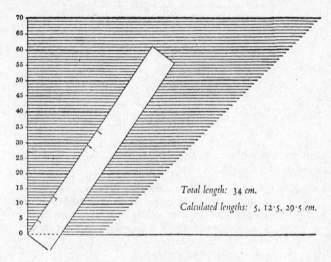

Total length: 34 *cm.*

Calculated lengths: 5, 12·5, 29·5 *cm.*

FIG. 23. A method of calculating lengths

A simpler procedure is shown in Figure 24, p. 170. This is a modification of one used at the laboratory of the Freshwater Biological Association, Windermere, and probably gives slightly more accurate results than the card method described above. Briefly, this apparatus consists of a solid foundation on which a semicircular board rotates. The semicircular board is covered with graph-paper which is marked in a manner similar to that shown in Figure 24, p. 170; this board rotates on a spindle and on its upper surface a long piece of plate glass rotates independently on the same spindle. A line is scratched on the lower surface of this glass, so as to pass through the centre of the hole on which the spindle rotates. The image of the scale is projected on to the semicircular board, and the board moved so that the spindle rests in the centre of the scale image, i.e. in the middle of its first growth-ring. The movable semicircular board is then rotated until the apex of the scale image touches, on the graph-paper, the line which represents the length of the fish at capture, in

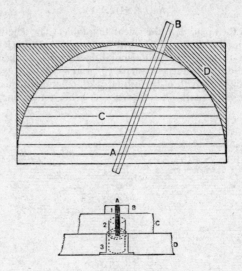

Fig. 24. Apparatus for calculating Yearly Lengths of Fish from Scale Reading

Above. A. Spindle on which rotates glass plate and semi-circle of teak; the scale image is so projected that the spindle is in the dead centre of the scale nucleus.

B. ⅛ plate glass with fine line scratched on lower surface.

C. Moveable hemisphere.

D. Foundation of 12 x plywood.

Below. Magnification of Spindle Mechanism (original) of Apparatus for calculating Yearly Lengths of Fish from scale reading. (1) Spindle of Silver Steel fitting closely into a brass spindle (2) which fits closely into an unmovable boss (3) screwed into the plywood. Note (2) does not extend to the surface of C.

the same way as the piece of card did in the other method. The plate glass is then rotated until the fine line on its lower surface crosses the apex of the scale image at its point of contact with the line representing the length of the fish at capture. The yearly lengths of the fish are read off along this line where the outer edge of the winter bands of rings cut the lines on the graph-paper (Jones, 1939).

BIBLIOGRAPHY

ALLEN, K. R. (1940); Studies on the biology of the early stages of the Salmon (*Salmo salar*). No. 1: Growth in the river Eden. *J. Anim. Ecol. 9:* 1–23. (1941); Idem. No. 2: Feeding habits. *Ibid. 10:* 47–76; (1941). Idem No. 3: Growth in the Thurso River System Caithness. *Ibid. 10:* 273–95. (1951); The Horokiwi Stream. *N. Zealand Mar. Dep. Fish. Bull.* No. 10; 231.

ALM, G. (1934); Salmon in the Baltic Precincts. *Rapp. Cons. Explor. Mer. 92:* 1–42. (1943); Fertilization experiments with salmon parr. *Rep. Inst. Freshwater Res. Drottningholm.* No. 22; 1–40. (1955); Artificial hybridization between different species of the salmon family. *Ibid.* No. 36; 13–54.

ARWIDSSON, I. (1910); Zur Kenntnis der Lebensgeschichte der jungen Lachse in den Flussen vor der Hinabwanderung ins Meer. *Pub. de Circ. 54:* 1–86.

BELDING, D. L. (1934). The Spawning Habits of the Atlantic Salmon. *Trans. Amer. Fish. Soc. 64:* 211–18.

BERG, L. S. (1932–33); Les poissons des eaux douces de l'U.R.S.S. et de pays limitrophes; 3e. edition revue et augmentée; partie 1 (in Russian.) Leningrad 8 vo. 543.

BERRY, J. (1932-33); Weed Control. *Avon. Biol. Res. Ann. Rep.* 32–35. (1933–34); Spawning Redds. *Ibid.* 7–11. (1935–36); Chemical control of Aquatic Weed. *Ibid.* 96–102.

BERT, P. (1871); Sur les phenomènes et les causes de la mort des animaux d'eau douce que l'on plonge dans l'eau de mer. *C. R. Acad. Sci. 73:* 382–464.

BEVELANDER, G. (1935); Comparative Study of Branchial epithelium in Fishes with Special Reference to extrarenal secretion. *J. Morph. Philad. 57:* 335–48. (1936); Branchial Glands in Fishes. *J. Morph. Philad. 59:* 215–22.

BHATIA, D. (1931); Factors involved in the production of annual zones on the scales of Rainbow Trout (*Salmo irideus*). 1. *J. exper. Zool. 59:* 45–59. (1931); Idem 2. *J. exper. Biol. 9:* 6–12.

BLAIR, A. A. (1942); Regeneration of the Scales of Atlantic Salmon. *J. Fish. Res. Bd. Can. 5:* 440–47.

BLAIR, W. F., BLAIR, A. P., BRODKORB, P., CAGLE, F. R., and MOORE, G. A. (1957). Vertebrates of the United States. McGraw-Hill, New York.

BRETT, J. R. (1952); Temperature Tolerance in Young Pacific Salmon. Genus *Oncorhynchus*. *J. Fish. Res. Bd. Can. 9:* 265–323. (1956); Some Principles of the Thermal requirements of Fishes. *Quart. Rev. Biol. 31:* 75–87.

BRETT, J. R., and MACKINNON, D. (1954); Some observations on olfactory perception in migrating adult Coho and Spring salmon. *J. Fish. Res. Bd. Can. 11:* 310–18.

BUCKLAND, F. (1880); Natural History of British Fishes. Unwin Bros. S.P.C.K.

BULL, H. O. (1930); The smolt descent of the River Tyne. *Dove Marine Laboratory, Cullercoats, Rep. (n.s.) 19:*

CAIN, A. J. (1953); Geography, Ecology & Co-existence in Relation to the Biological definition of Species. *Evolution, 7:* 76–83.

CALDERWOOD, W. L. (1905); The White Spot Disease in Salmon in the Island of Lewis. *Fish. Bd. Scot. Ann. Rep. 24:* (Appendix V) 78–79. (1931); Salmon Hatching and Salmon Migrations. Arnold, London. (1945); Passage of Smolts through Turbines. *Salm. & Trout Mag. London*, No. 115: 214–21.

CARPENTER, K. (1940); The Feeding of Salmon Parr in the Cheshire Dee. *Proc. Zool. Soc. Lond.* (A) *110:* 81–96.

CARR, A. M. (1913). Report on samples of Parr and Smolts from the Wye and its tributaries the Irfon and Ithon caught in May, July and October, 1912. *Fish. Invest.* (1) *1:* (Appendix 2), 109–11.

CHAISSON, A. F. (1933); Adaptation of Salmon and Trout Fry in Tidal Waters. *Rep. Biol. Bd. Can.* 17–18.

CLEMENTS, W. A., FOERSTER, R. E., and PRITCHARD, A. L. (1939); Migration and Conservation of Salmon. Migration of Pacific Salmon in British Columbia waters. *Publ. Amer. Soc. Adv. Sci.* No. 8; 51–59.

COLLINS, G. B. (1952); Factors Influencing the Orientation of migrating Anadromous Fishes. *Fish. Bull. U.S. 52:* 375–96.

COSTON, TOWNER, H. E., PENTELOW, F. T. K., and BUTCHER, R. W. (1936); River Management. Seeley Service, London, 263.

CREASER, C. W. (1926); The structure and growth of the scales of fishes in relation to the interpretation of their life-history, with special reference to the sunfish *Eupomotis gibbosus*. *Misc. Publ. Mus. Zool. Univ. Mich.* No. 17; 1–82.

CRICHTON, M. I. (1935); Scale Absorption in Salmon and Sea Trout. *Fish. Scot. Salmon Fish.* No. 4: 1–8.

DAHL, K. (1907); The scales of Herring as a means of determining Age, Growth and Migration. *Rep. Norwegian Fish Invest. 2:* (6) 135–47. (1911); The Age and Growth of Salmon and Trout in Norway as shown by their Scales. (Engl. Trans.) Salm. & Trout Ass., London. 1–141. (1928);

The dwarf salmon of Lake Byglandsfjord. *Salm. and Trout Mag. London. 51:* 108–12.

DAHL, K., and SØMME, S. (1942); Salmon Marking in Norway. 1938, '39 and '40. *Skrift. Norske Vidensk.-Akad. Oslo.* (1941) No. 10; 1–52.

DAHL, K., and SØMME, O. M. (1944); Sexual Maturing of Salmon (*Salmo salar* L.) *Ibid.* (1944) No. 7; 3–41.

DAVIS, H. S. (1946). Care and Diseases of Trout. *U.S. Dep. Int. Fish Wildlife Serv. Res. Rep.* No. 12; 98.

DAY, F. (1887). British and Irish Salmonidae. Williams & Norgate, London.

DYMOND, J. R. and VLADYKOV, V. D. (1933); The distribution and relationship of the Salmonoid fishes of North America and North Asia. *Proc. Fifth Pacific Sci. Cong.* (5) 3741–3750.

ELLIS, W. G., and JONES, J. W. (1939); The activity of the Spermatozoa of *Salmo salar* in relation to Osmotic Pressure. *J. Exper. Biol. 16:* 530–34.

FABRICIUS, E. (1953); Aquarium Observation on the Spawning Behaviour of the Char, *Salmo alpinus. Rept. Inst. Freshwater Res. Drottningholm, 34:* 14–48.

FOERSTER, R. E. (1934); An investigation, etc., No. 4. The Life-cycle of the 1925 year-class with Natural Propagation. *Contrib. Canad. Biol.* (n.s.) *8:* 347–55. (1936); An investigation etc., No. 5. The Life-History cycle of the 1926 year-class with Artificial Propagation. *J. Biol. Bd. Can. 2:* 311–33. (1936); Return from the sea of Sockeye salmon, *Oncorhynchus nerka,* with special reference to percentage survival. *Ibid. 3:* 26–42. (1946); Restocking depleted Sockeye salmon areas by transfer of eggs. *J. Fish. Res. Bd. Can. 7:* (6) 483–90. (1954); On the relation of adult Sockeye salmon (*Oncorhynchus nerka*) returns to known smolt seaward migrations. *Ibid. 11:* (4) 339–50.

FOERSTER, R. E., and PRITCHARD, A. L. (1934); Report on the Marking of Pink Salmon Fingerlings at Cultus Lake in 1932. *Biol. Bd. Can. Ann. Rep.* 1933: 83–84.

FOERSTER R. E. and RICKER, W. E. (1940); The Effect of Reduction of Predacious Fish on survival of young Sockeye Salmon at Cultus Lake. *J. Fish. Res. Bd. Can. 5:* (4) 315–36. (1953); The Coho salmon of Cultus Lake and Sweltzer Creek. *Ibid.* (10) 293–319.

FONTAINE, M. (1948); Physiologie du Saumon. *Ann. Stat. Centr. Hydrobiol. appl. 2:* 153–88.

FONTAINE, M., LACHIVER, F., LELOUP, J., and OLIVEREAU, M. (1948). La fonction thyroïdienne du saumon *Salmo salar* L., au cours de sa migration reproductrice. *J. Physiologie, 40:* 182–84.

FONTAINE, M., and VIBERT, R. (1952). Migration fluviale anadrome du Saumon (*Salmo salar* L.) et gradient de salinité. *Ann. Sta. Cent. Hydrobiol. appl. 4:* 339–46.

FORD, E. B. (1945). Polymorphism. *Biol. Rev. 20:* 73–83.

FRANKS, R. (1656). Northern Memoirs calculated for the Meridian of Scotland. Constable, Edinburgh, 2nd ed. 1821, 166–176.

FRIEND, G. F. (1941); The Life-History and Ecology of the Salmon Gill Maggot, *Salmincola salmonea. Trans. Roy. Soc. Edin. 60:* (Part II, No. 15) 503–43.

FROST, W. E., and WENT, A. E. J. (1940); River Liffey Survey III. The Growth and Food of Young Salmon. *Proc. Roy. Irish Acad.* (B) *46:* (4) 53–80.

FURUNCULOSIS COMMITTEE (1930); Interim Report of the Furunculosis Committee. H.M. Stationery Office, London. (1933); Second Interim Report of the Furunculosis Committee. H.M. Stationery Office, London.

GRAY, J. (1937); Pseudorheotropism in Fishes. *J. Exper. Biol.* London, *14:* 95–103.

GREEN, C. W. (1915); On some Quantitative Physiological Changes in the Pacific Salmon during the run to the Spawning Grounds. *Trans. Amer. Fish. Soc. 45:* 5–12. (1919); Biochemical changes in the Muscle Tissue of King Salmon during the fast of Spawning Migration. *J. Biol. Chem. 39:* 435–56. (1921); Chemical development of the ovaries of King Salmon during the spawning migration. *Ibid. 48:* 59–71.

GRIFFIN, P. J., SNIESZKO, S. F., and FRIDDLE, S. B. (1952); A more comprehensive description of *Bacterium salmonicida. Trans. Amer. Fish Soc. 82:* 129–38.

GUNTHER, A. (1864); Catalogue of Fishes in the British Museum. Taylor and Francis, London.

GUSTELL, J. S., and SNIESZKO, S. F. (1948); Furunculosis in fish: its diagnosis and treatment. *Vet. Med. 43:* 484–86. (1949); Dosage of sulfamerazine in the treatment of furunculosis of brook trout *Salvelinus fontinalis. Trans. Amer. Fish Soc. 76* (1946): 82–96.

HAIG-BROWN, R. (1952); Canadian Pacific Salmon. Dept. Fish Canad. Ottawa. (Reprinted from *Canad. Geographical J.*). 5–23.

HALLIDAY, (1824); Report of the Salmon Commission 1824. See: *British & Irish Salmonidae,* Day, (1887), 81.

HANAVAN, M. G., and SKUD, B. E. (1954); Intertidal Spawning of Pink Salmon. *U.S. Dep. Int. Fish Wildlife Serv. Fish. Bull. 56:* (95) 167–85.

HASLER, A. D., and WISBY, W. J. (1951); Discrimination of stream odours by fishes and its relation to parent stream behaviour. *Amer. Nat. 85:* (823) 223–38.

HASLER, A. D. (1954); Odour perception and orientation in fishes. *J. Fish. Res. Bd. Canad. 11:* (2) 107–29. (1956); Perception of Pathways by fishes in Migration. *Quart. Rev. Biol. 31:* (3) 200–09.

HAYES, F. R. (1946); Inland Fisheries Investigations. *Rep. Nova Scotia Dep. Industry, 1946:* 43–44. (1953); Artificial Freshets and Other Factors Controlling the Ascent and Population of Atlantic Salmon in the La Have River, Nova Scotia. *Publ. Fish. Res. Bd. Canad. Bull.* No. 99; 1–47.

HIGGS, A. (1942); Big Trout from Big Eggs. *Salmon & Trout Mag.* London, No. 106; 216–30.

HOAGLAND, H. (1935); Pacemakers in relation to aspects of behaviour. MacMillan, New York.

HOAR, W. F. (1942); Diurnal variations in feeding activity of young salmon and trout. *J. Fish. Res. Bd. Canad. 6:* (1) 90–101. (1951); The Behaviour of Chum, Pink and Coho Salmon in Relation to their Seaward Migration. *Ibid. 8:* (4) 241–63. (1952); Thyroid Function in Some Anadromous and Land-locked Teleosts. *Trans. Roy. Soc. Canad.* (3) *46:* 39–53. (1954); The Behaviour of Juvenile Pacific Salmon, with particular reference to the Sockeye, (*Oncorhynchus nerka*). *J. Fish. Res. Bd. Canad. 11:* (1) 69–97. (1956); Behaviour of Migrating Pink and Chum Salmon Fry. *Ibid.* 13: (3) 309–25.

HOAR, W. S., and BELL, G. M. (1950); The thyroid gland in relation to the seaward migration of Pacific salmon. *Canad. J. Res.* (D) *28:* 126–36.

HOAR, W. S., BLACK, V. S., and BLACK, E. C. (1951); Some Aspects of the Physiology of Fish. *Publ. Ontario Fish Res. Lab.* No. 71; 1–35.

HOBBS, D. F. (1937); Natural Reproduction of Quinnat Salmon, Brown and Rainbow Trout, in certain New Zealand Waters. *Fish. Bull. Marine Dep. Wellington, N.Z.* No. 6; 1–104.

HULT, J., and JOHNELS, A. (1949); Predators on Salmon Fry in the River Mörrumsa in 1948. *Inst. Freshwater Res. Drottningholm, Rep.* No. 29; 45–48.

HUNTSMAN, A. G. (1918); The scale method of calculating the rate of growth in fishes. *Trans. Roy. Soc. Canad.* (3) *12:* (4) 47–52. (1933); St. John Salmon—the earliest run known. *Atlantic Biol. Station, No. 25, Rep.* No. 6; 7–10. (1936); Return of Salmon from the Sea. *Biol. Bd. Canad. Bull.* No. 51: 1–20. (1938); Sea Movement of Canadian Atlantic Salmon Kelts. *J. Fish. Res. Bd. Canad. 4:* (2) 96–135. (1939); The Migration and Conservation of Salmon. *Publ. Amer. Assoc. Adv. Sci. 8:* 32–44. (1939); Races and Homing Instinct. *Salmon & Trout Mag. London,* 3–7. (1941); Cyclical abundance and birds versus salmon. *J. Fish. Res. Bd. Canad. 5:* (3) 227–35. (1942); Death of Salmon and Trout with High Temperature. *Ibid. 5:* (5) 485–501. (1945); Migration of Salmon Parr. *Ibid. 6:* (5) 399–402. (1945); Variable Seaward Migration of Salmon. *Ibid. 6:* (4) 311–25. (1948); Freshets and Fish. *Trans. Amer. Fish Soc. 75:* (1945) 257–66.

HUNTSMAN, A. G., and HOAR, W. S. (1939); Resistance of Atlantic Salmon to Sea Water. *J. Fish. Res. Bd. Canad. 4:* (5) 409–11.

HUTTON, J. A. (1922). The Mortality among Wye Salmon after Spawning. *Salmon & Trout Mag. London,* (Jan. 1922); 4–33. (1923); The Parasites of

Salmon. *Ibid.* (Dec. 1923); 1–11. (1924); The Life-History of the Salmon. Aberdeen, University Press. (1937); Wye Parr and Smolts. The Inverse ratio theory of River and Sea Life. *Salmon & Trout Mag. London,* (June 1937) No. 87; 3–7.

HUXLEY, J. S. (1930); Maladaptation of Trout Sperm to Freshwater. *Nature, London, 125:* 494. (1955); Morphism and Evolution. *Heredity, 9:* 1–52.

HYNES, H. B. N. (in the press); The Biology of Polluted Waters. Liverpool Univ. Press, Liverpool.

JARVI, T. H. (1920); Die Kleine Maräne (*Coregonus albula* L.) im Keitelesee, eine ökologische und ökonomische Studie. *Ann. Acad. Sci. Fenn.* (A) *14:* No. 1; 302.

JONES, J. W. (1939); Salmon of the Cheshire Dee. 1937 and 1938. *Trans. Livp. Biol. Soc. 52:* 19–79. [1939] (Unpublished); The fauna of some species of weed from Southern rivers. (1940). Histological changes in the Testes in the Sexual cycle of Male Salmon Parr (*Salmo salar* L.Juv.). *Proc. Roy. Soc. Lond.,* (B) 128: 499–509. (1947); Salmon Smolts and Salt Water. Survival of Smolts of *Salmo salar* at various rates of increased Salinity. *Salmon & Trout Mag. London,* No. 119: 63–76. (1947); Salmon and Trout Hybrids. *Proc. Zool. Soc. Lond. 117:* 708–15. (1949); Studies of the scales of Young Salmon (*Salmo salar* L.(Juv.)) in relation to Growth, Migration and Spawning. *Fish. Invest.* (1) *5:* 1–23. (1950); Salmon Studies. *Ibid.* (1) *5:* (2) 6–23. (1953); I. The Scales of Roach. II. Age and Growth of the Trout, Grayling Perch and Roach of Llyn Tegid (Bala) and the Roach of the River Birket. *Fish. Invest.* (1) *5:* (7) 7–18. (1953); Salmon Studies 1951. I. Salmon of the Cumberland Derwent 1951. II. Salmon of the Cheshire Dee, 1951. *Fish. Invest.* (1) *5:* (6) 3–10. 1958; Spawning grounds of Salmon. *Trout and Salm. Mag.* No. 35, (3), 5–6.

JONES, J. W., and BALL, J. N. (1954); The Spawning Behaviour of Brown Trout and Salmon. *Brit. J. Anim. Behav. 2:* 103–14.

JONES, J. W., and KING, G. M. (1946); Winter Salmon in the Dee. *Salmon & Trout Mag. London,* No. 117: 153–61. (1949); Experimental observations on the Spawning Behaviour of the Atlantic Salmon (*Salmo salar* Linn.). *Proc. Zool. Soc. Lond. 119:* 33–48. (1950); Further experimental observations on the Spawning Behaviour of Atlantic Salmon. *Ibid. 120:* 317–23. (1950); "Progeny of Male Salmon Parr. A comparison with those from Normal Adults." *Salm. & Trout Mag. London,* No. 128; 24–27. (1952); The Spawning of the Male Salmon Parr (*Salmo salar* Linn. Juv.). *Proc. Zool. Soc. Lond. 122:* 615–19.

JONES, J. W., and ORTON, J. H. (1940); The Paedogenetic male cycle in *Salmo salar* L. *Proc. Roy. Soc. Lond.* (B) *128:* 485–99.

JORDAN, S. (1925); Fishes. Appleton and Co., New York.

KEYS, A., and WILMER, E. N. (1932); Chloride Secreting Cells in the Gills of

Fishes with special reference to the Common Eel. *J. Physiol. Cambr.* **76:** 368–78.

KEYS, A. (1932–33); Adaptation to Varying Salinity in the Common Eel. *Proc. Roy. Soc. Lond.* (B) *112:* 184–200.

LANDGREBE, F. W. (1941); The role of the pituitary and the thyroid in the development of teleosts. *J. Exper. Biol. 18:* 162–69.

LEE, R. (1920); A review of the methods of age and growth determination in fishes by means of scales. *Fish. Invest. 4:* (2) 1–32.

MACINTYRE, D. (1947); Furred and Feathered Robbers: Some Observations on Seals and Cormorants. *Salm. & Trout Mag. London,* No. 121; 248–50.

MACKINNON, D., and HOAR, W. S. (1953); Responses of Coho and Chum Salmon fry to current. *J. Fish. Res. Bd. Canad. 10:* (8) 523–38.

MCKENZIE, R. A. (1935); Cod fish in captivity. *Biol. Bd. Canad. Prog. Rep. Atl.* No. 16; 7–10.

MALLOCH, P. D. H. (1910); Life-History of the Salmon, Trout and other Freshwater Fish. A. & C. Black, London.

MALLOCH, W. (1956); Personal Communication.

MENZIES, W. J. M. (1926); Salmon of the Grimersta, Lewis 1925. *Fish. Bd. Scot. Salmon Fish.* No. 6: 1–14. (1931); The Salmon, Its Life Story. Blackwood, London. (1939); The Migration and Conservation of Salmon. Some preliminary observations on the Migrations of the European Salmon. *Publ. Amer. Ass. Adv. Sci. 8:* 13–25. (1947); "On the Spawning of Salmon." *Salmon & Trout Mag. London,* No. 120: 130–32. (1949); The Stock of Salmon, Its Migrations, Preservation and Improvement. Arnold, London.

MONASTYRSKY, G. N. (1926); Concerning the method of the growth-rate determination in fishes from the measurements of their scales. Siberian Ichthyological Lab.

NALL, G. H. (1930); Life of the Sea Trout. Seeley Service & Co., London.

NEAVE, F. (1936); Development of the Scales of Salmo. *Proc. Trans. Roy. Soc. Canad. 30:* (5) 55–72.

O'MEALLAIN, S. (1951); Fish Pass at Leixlip Dam, River Liffey Hydro-Electric Development. *J. Dep. Agric. Irish Free State* 3–10.

ORTON, J. H., JONES J. W., and KING, G. M. (1938). The Male Sexual Stage in Salmon Parr (*Salmo salar* L. Juv.). *Proc. Roy. Soc. Lond.* (B) 125: 103–14.

PATON, N. (1898); Report of Investigations on the Life-History of the Salmon in Freshwater. *Fish. Bd. Scot. Salmon Fish.,* 1–176.

PATTERSON, J. H. (1903); The Cause of Salmon Disease. *Fish. Bd. Scot. Salmon Fish.,* 1–52.

PENTELOW, F. T. K. (1953). River Purification. Arnold, London.

PENTELOW, F. T. K., and BASSINDALE, R. (1933); The proportion of the sexes and food of smolts of salmon and sea-trout in the Tees estuary. Fish Invest. 1, 3, (4) 1–14.

POWERS, E. B. (1939); Chemical factors affecting the migratory movements of Pacific Salmon. The Migration and Conservation of Salmon. *Pub. Amer. Ass. Adv. Sci. 8:* 72–85. (1941); Physico-chemical behaviour of waters as factors in the "homing" of the Salmon. *Ecology, Brooklyn, 22:* 1–16.

POWERS, E. B., and CLARK, R. T. (1943); Further evidence on chemical factors affecting the migratory movements of fishes, especially the Salmon. *Ibid. 24:* 109–13.

PRITCHARD, A. L. (1938); Transplantation of Pink Salmon (*Oncorhynchus gorbuscha*) into Masset Inlet, B.C. in the Barren Years. *J. Fish. Res. Bd. Canad. 4* (2) 141–50. (1947); Efficiency of Natural Propagation of the Pink Salmon (*O. gorbuscha*) in McClinton Creek, Masset Inlet, B.C. *Ibid. 7:* (5) 224–36.

PRYCE-TANNATT, T. E. (1938); Fish passes in connection with obstructions in salmon rivers. Arnold, London, 108.

PYEFINCH, K. A. (1955); A review of the literature on the biology of the Atlantic Salmon, *Salmo salar* Linn. *Sci. Invest, Freshwater Fish. Scot.* No. 9; 1–24.

REGAN, Tate C. (1911); British Freshwater Fishes. Methuen, London. (1920); The Geographical Distribution of Salmon and Trout. *Salm. and Trout Mag. London,* No. 22: 25–35. (1938); A ripe female salmon parr. *Fishing Gazette, London,* No. 116: 298.

RICH, W. H., and HOLMES, H. B. (1929). Experiments in marking young Chinook Salmon on the Columbia River, 1916–27. *Bull. U.S. Bur. Fish. 44:* 215–64.

RICH, W. H. (1939). Local populations and migration in relation to the Conservation of Pacific Salmon in the Western States of Alaska. Migration and Conservation of Salmon. *Publ. Amer. Ass. Adv. Sci. 8:* 45–50.

RICKER, W. E. (1938). Residual and Kokanee salmon in Cultus Lake. *J. Fish. Res. Bd. Canad. 4:* (3) 192–218. (1941); The Consumption of Young Sockeye Salmon by Predacious Fish. *Ibid. 5:* (3) 293–313.

ROBERTS, C. H., and JEE, E. C. (1922); The influence of salt on fresh-water fish. *Min. Ag. & Fish. Standing Committee on River Pollution. Rep. 38.*

ROULE, L. (1933); Fishes, Journeys and Migrations. Routledge, London.

RUDD, J. A. (1946). Big Trout from Big Eggs. *Salmon & Trout Mag. London,* No. 116; 32–36.

SCHEER, B. T. (1939); Homing Instinct in Salmon. *Quart. Rev. Biol. 14:* 408–30.

SETNA, S. B. (1934); Development of the Trout scales. *J. Univ. Bombay* (Biol. Sci.) *2:* (5) 17–32.

SHAW, J. (1840); Account of Experimental Observation on the Development and Growth of Salmon Fry, etc. *Trans. Roy. Soc. Edinb. 14:* 547–66.

SHERRIFF, C. W. M. (1922). Herring investigations. Report on the mathematical analysis of random samples of herrings. *Fish. Bd. Scot. Sci. Invest.* No. 1; 1–25.

SNIESZKO, S. F. (1953); Therapy of Bacterial Fish Diseases. *Trans. Amer. Fish. Soc. 88:* 313–30.

SOUTHERN, R. (1933). Do Salmon ever Spawn before they go to Sea? *The Field,* London, June.

SPIERS, J. M. (1948); Summary of Literature on Aquatic Weed control. *Canadian Fish Culturist, 3:* (4) 20–32.

STUART, T. A. (1953); Spawning Migration, Reproduction and Young Stages of Loch Trout (*Salmo trutta* L.) *Scottish Home Dep. Freshwater and Salm. Fish. Res. Rep.* No. 5; 3–39.

SULLIVAN, C. M. (1954); Temperature reception and Responses in Fish. *J. Fish. Res. Bd. Canad. 11:* (2) 153–70.

SVARDSON, G. (1945). Chromosome studies on the Salmonidae. *Rep. Inst. Freshwater Res. Drottningholm,* No. 23; 1–151.

SWIFT, D. R. (1955); Seasonal variation in growth-rate, thyroid gland activity and food reserve of Brown Trout, *Salmo trutta* Linn. *J. Exper. Biol. 32:* 751–64.

TCHERNAVIN, V. (1938); Changes in the Salmon Skull. *Trans. Zool. Soc. Lond. 24:* 104–84. (1939); The origin of Salmon, its ancestry marine or freshwater? *Salm. Trout Mag. London,* No. 95: 120–40.

THOMPSON, W. F. (1945). Effect of the obstruction at Hell's gate on the Sockeye salmon of the Frazer River. *Int. Pacif. Salm. Fish. Comm. Bull.* No. 1: 1–175.

TINBERGEN, N. (1948); Social releasers and the experimental method required for their study. *Wilson Bull. 60:* 6–52. (1951); The Study of Instinct. Oxford. (1952); Derived Activities, their Causation, Biological Significance, Origin, and Emancipation during Evolution. *Quart. Rev. Biol. 27:* 1–32.

TINBERGEN, N., and van IERSEL, J. J. A. (1947); Displacement reactions in the three-spined stickleback. *Behaviour, 1:* 56–63.

TURING, H. D. (1952); River Pollution. A.C.A., London.

VAN OOSTEN, J. (1923); A study of the scales of whitefishes of known ages. *Zoologica, N.Y. 2:* 380–412. (1929); Life-History of the Lake Herring (*Leucichthys artedi* Le Sueur) of Lake Huron as revealed by its scales, with Critique of the Scale Method. *Dept. Commerce U.S.A. Bur. Fish. 44:* (Doc. 1053) 265–428. (1941); Age and Growth of Freshwater Fishes. A Symposium on Hydrobiology, Madison. 196–205.

VAN SOMEREN, V. D. (1940); The Factors Conditioning the rising of Trout, *Salmo trutta,* in a small Freshwater Lake. *J. Anim. Ecol. 9:* 89–106. (1952);

The Biology of Trout in Kenya Colony. Government Printer, Nairobi, 1–110.

WALSH, C. F. (1863). Quoted by Frank Buckland *in* Fish Hatching. Tinsley Bros., London.

WARD, H. B. (1932); The Origin of the Land-locked Habit in Salmon. *Proc. Nat. Acad. Sci. Philad. 18:* 569–80. (1939); Salmon Psychology. *J. Wash. Acad. Sci. 29:* 1–14. (1939); Factors controlling salmon migration. No. 8 Migration and conservation of Salmon. *Publ. Amer. Assoc. Adv. Sci. 8:* 60–71.

WENT, A. E. J. (1938); Salmon of the River Shannon. *Proc. Roy. Irish Acad.* (B) *44:* 261–322. (1943); Salmon of the River Shannon. *Ibid. 49:* 151–175. (1946); Salmon of the River Shannon, 1944 and 1945. *J. Anim. Ecol. 15:* 155–69. (1947); Value of the Kelt: Some Notes on Previously-Spawned Salmon in Ireland. *Salm. & Trout Mag. London,* No. 119: 41–48. (1949); Spring Fish. Are there two types of Winter Salmon? *Salm. & Trout Mag. London,* No. 125: 23–26. (1951); "Movements of Salmon around Ireland." *Proc. Roy. Irish Acad.* (B) *54:* 169–201. (1953); "Movements of Salmon around Ireland." *Ibid. 55:* 209–23. (1955); Irish salmon and salmon fisheries. Arnold, London.

WENT, A. E. J., and FROST, W. E. (1942); River Liffey Survey, V. Growth of Brown Trout (*Salmo trutta* L.) in Alkaline and Acid Waters. *Proc. Roy. Irish Acad.* (B) *48:* 67–84.

WHITE, H. C. (1934); Some facts and theories concerning the Atlantic salmon. *Trans. Amer. Fish. Soc. 64:* 360–62. (1936); Homing of Salmon in Apple River, N.S. *J. Biol. Bd. Canad. 2:* (4) 391–400. (1939); Factors influencing the descent of Atlantic salmon smolts. *Ibid. 4:* 323–326. (1942); Atlantic Salmon redds and Artificial spawning beds. *J. Fish. Res. Bd. Canad. 6:* (1) 37–44. (1957); Food and natural history of Mergansers on Salmon waters in the maritime provinces of Canada. *Fish. Res. Bd. Can., Bull.* No. 116: 1–63.

WHITE, H. C., and HUNTSMAN, A. G. (1938); Is local behaviour in Salmon heritable? *J. Fish. Res. Bd. Canad. 4:* (1) 1–18.

WHITE, M. J. D. (1954); Animal Cytology and Evolution. Univ. Press, Cambridge.

WIEBE, A. H. (1930); Notes on the exposure of young fishes to varying concentrations of Arsenic. *Trans. Amer. Fish. Soc. 60:* 270–78.

WILLIAMSON, I. (1928); Furunculosis of the Salmonidae. *Fish. Bd. Scot. Salm. Fish.* No. 5: 1–17.

WISBY, W. J., and HASLER, A. D. (1954); Effect of olfactory occlusion on migratory silver salmon *O. kisutch. J. Fish. Res. Bd. Canad. 11:* (4) 472–78.

WISDOM, A. S. (1956). The Law on the Pollution of Waters. Shaw & Sons, London, 296.

YOUNG, A. (1849). *See* Day (1887) 80–81. London, Williams & Norgate.

ADDENDUM

The following more recent publications not referred to in the text may be of interest:

HOAR, W. S. (1958); Rapid learning of a constant course by travelling schools of juvenile Pacific Salmon. *J. Fish. Res. Bd. Canada* (*15*) No. 2. 251–274.

HOAR, W. S. (1958); The evolution of migratory behaviour among juvenile salmon of the genus *Oncorhyncus*. *J. Fish. Res. Bd. Canada* (*15*) No. 3. 391–428.

HOAR, W. S. (1958); The analysis of behaviour of fish. The Investigation of Fish-Power Problems. *MacMillan Lectures in Fisheries. Univ. of B.C. Vancouver.*

HASLER, A. D., HORRALL, R. H., WISBY, W. S. and BRAEMER, W. (1958); Sun Orientation and Homing in Fishes. *Limnology and Oceanography* (*3*) No. 4. 353–361.

ACKNOWLEDGEMENTS

THE author and publisher gratefully acknowledge the kind permission given for the use of the following line drawings:

Fig. 1: from Jones, 1949; Salmon and Trout Hybrids. *Proc. Zool. Soc. Lond. 117.* Figs. 3, 6, 7: from Jones, 1950; *Fish. Invest (1)5.* Figs. 4, 9, 24: from Jones, 1939; Salmon of the Cheshire Dee. *Trans. Livp. Biol. Soc. 52.* Figs. 5, 22, 23: from Nall 1930; Life of the Sea Trout. *Seeley, Service and Co. Lond.* Fig. 10: from Jones, 1951; Salmon Studies. *Fish Invest.* (1) 5 (6). Fig. 11: from Tchernavin, 1939; Changes in the Salmon Skull. *Trans. Zool. Soc. Lond. 24.* Figs. 12, 13: from Jones and Ball, 1954; The Spawning Behaviour of Brown Trout and Salmon. *Brit. J. Anim. Behav. 2* Figs. 14, 15: from Jones and Orton, 1940; The Paedogenetic male cycle in *Salmo salar L. Proc. Roy. Soc. Lond. 128.* Figs. 16, 17: from Jones, 1958; *Trout and Salmon Mag. 35 vol. 3.* Figs. 18, 19, 20: from Friend, 1941; The Life History and Ecology of the Salmon Gill Maggot. *Trans Roy. Soc. Edin. 60 Part 11 No. 15.* Fig. 21: from Mellanby, 1948; Animal Life in Fresh Water (3rd edition). *Methuen. Lond.*

GENERAL INDEX

INDEX OF AUTHORS CITED